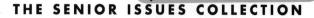

THE SENIOR ISSUES COLLECTION

COLLECTION EDITOR:
GILLDA LEITENBERG

MATTERS OF GENDER

EDITED BY GRETA HOFMANN NEMIROFF

To my sister, Herta,
my first and greatest teacher.

McGraw-Hill Ryerson Limited

Toronto • New York • Auckland • Bogotá
Caracas • Lisbon • London • Madrid • Mexico • Milan
New Delhi • San Juan • Singapore • Sydney • Tokyo

Matters of Gender
The Senior Issues Collection

Copyright © McGraw-Hill Ryerson Limited, 1996
All rights reserved. No part of this publication may be reproduced or transmitted in any form or by any means, or stored in a data base or retrieval system, without the prior written permission of McGraw-Hill Ryerson Limited.

ISBN 0-07-551700-0

1 2 3 4 5 6 7 8 9 10   BG   5 4 3 2 1 0 9 8 7 6

Printed and bound in Canada

Care has been taken to trace ownership of copyright material contained in this text. The publishers will gladly accept any information that will enable them to rectify any reference or credit in subsequent editions.

Canadian Cataloguing in Publication Data

Main entry under title:

Matters of gender

(The senior issues collection)
ISBN 0-07-551700-0

1. Readers (Secondary). 2. Readers – Sex role.
3. Sex role – Literary collections. I. Nemiroff,
Greta Hofmann, date. II. Series.

PE1127.S4M37 1995   808'.0427   C95-932409-7

Editor: *Kathy Evans*
Supervising Editor: *Nancy Christoffer*
Permissions Editor: *Jacqueline Donovan*
Production Co-ordinator: *Yolanda Pigden*
Proofreader: *Gail Marsden*
Designer: *Mary Opper*
Typesetter: *Pages Design Ltd.*
Cover Illustrator: *Simon Ng*

The editors wish to thank reviewer Freda Appleyard for her comments and advice.

This book was manufactured in Canada using acid-free and recycled paper.

Contents

Introduction

One of the first facts that is established in a police report is the gender of the suspect. Gender mediates our expectations of appearance as much as do language, height, weight, skin, and hair colour. In senior high school, gender is a matter of concern and interest; at least it certainly was in the 1950s when I was a high school student in Montreal, and I doubt that the world has changed very much in that respect.

Because one of the jobs of young people is to grow into adults, matters of gender are going to influence how you imagine your adult life to be, and how you would like to participate in adult society as women or men. In order to make appropriate decisions about your adulthood, you also must understand the other sex...how the other half experiences this world.

I have organized this anthology around various themes which relate to the experiences of both genders: growing up male or female; the body and how we think of it; love...our hopes, expectations, and disappointments; marriage, its joys and sorrows; the traditional family and current transitions within the family; the world of work; and finally, empowerment and transformation...the possibilities for change. Other themes are woven into the collection, such as education and learning, play, how we experience nature, and some of the painful truths about racism and exploitation in the world.

In our society, males and females grow up, often within the same families, with different sets of experiences and expectations. They also share many experiences and expectations. I have chosen works for this anthology which illustrate both differences and similarities. However, that is not the only reason I have chosen these particular works. I have also chosen them because I consider them to be well and interestingly written, because I like them.

There are works in this book by writers from throughout Canada and from other countries in the world. It is my opinion that we in

Canada are privileged to be living in a country which is in a process of reinventing itself as a society inclusive of a growing diversity of peoples. For this reason, I have been pleased to include works by writers from numerous ethnicities written in English and in translation as well. I am also glad to have found a relevant work on sexual orientation, a subject of importance to young people.

Sometimes it may be difficult for the readers to imagine why some pieces have been chosen for a book organized on the theme of gender. You might want to think about what the gender norms are in the society being described and in your own social context. It might be helpful to ask yourselves what the works themselves say about being male or female. Finally, you might refer back to your own lives and what your gender means to you in terms of the social restrictions you may experience along with your dreams and ambitions for your own life.

In selecting the works for Matters of Gender, *I have been most hopeful that in reading this book, students would increase the range of possibilities in your own lives and in your understanding of the lives and choices of others. If there is any underlying message to the structure of the book, it is* vive la différence *of gender, race, ethnicity, religious faith, and sexual orientation. There is a fascination and a beauty in the ways in which different cultures and individuals respond to both tradition and transition in gender roles in their particular societies.*

May this book keep you reading; may it speak to your concerns; may it expand the circumference of your world!

Greta Hofmann Nemiroff

Notre Dame
de Grâce

～

BY

NAOMI

GUTTMAN

They trip out the corner store,
children in low heels. Jessica
fusses with her purse strap and big
Cindy lifts the milk carton
almost shoulder high.

(Things were heavier when I was small
and then I grew so fast it hurt.)
So why do I revert to
innocence is
ignorance is
when I see them straggle up the street?

Raids down our green-lined hill
to Sherbrooke Street, so tireless and uncertain
fringed with undershirted men
each one a lonely menace
on his own stone step. Summer days

when suddenly it seemed we all agreed
to go to Al's Variety. And there we bought
or stole those delectable packets
of coloured sugar, sharing their synthetic tartness
under our mothers' balconies

till our tongues were sore, our fingers
stained with evidence. How we yearned
for womanly bodies, for danger in our lives.

And these girls? If they notice me they
see a neighbour, arms full
of groceries. Old and stupid,
or do I know something? Perhaps a secret—
their progress up the street,
the cries to come at night.

Shaping a Young Male Mind

BY

BRONWEN

WALLACE

~

My son started back to school today. As I watched him race off, so nonchalantly, on his 10-speed, I felt that familiar mixture of longing and relief. Longing, because he has grown so fast, because he is only with me for such a short, short time; relief because the house is empty again, at last; I can have that second cup of coffee in peace and start work on the new story that's been filling my brain with its insistent racket.

But there was something else as well, another feeling, harder to define. My son is 13 now. More and more he looks to his peers and to grown men to teach him what he needs to learn about being a man in this culture. And as I watch him, watching the men who will be his role model, I wonder what he is seeing there.

I know what I *hope* he's learning and so, for the first day of school, I've prepared a sort of wish-list, especially for the mothers of sons.

In school, first of all. I know that in history class he will learn of the Great Heroes of his sex who founded colonies and fought wars to protect them, but I hope he learns, too, that the men who chose *not* to fight were heroes as well, not cowards or wimps. And I hope he learns

a little of what the women were doing all this time, that someone besides me reinforces the ideas that the history of the spinning wheel is as important as that of the rifle.

And in English class, whose stories will he hear? Will all the central characters be boys, having adventures? Or will there be girls as well, strong, active girls who like to climb trees and solve mysteries as much as some of their brothers like to stay home and paint pictures?

My son has already told me that one of the most important aspects of his education so far has been the opportunity to learn another language. He has enjoyed his bilingual program and he wants to continue it. I hope he'll be able to. I hope his perception—that learning French increases his appreciation of English because it increases his appreciation of language in general—is one that teachers and administrators listen to. I hope he's not a victim of the kind of bigotry that sees the wider understanding of another's culture as some sort of threat to one's own.

I'm glad to see that he already takes cooking and sewing as well as wood and metal working. *That's* an improvement, certainly, but I hope that in gym class he learns to dance as well as to play basketball. And in playing basketball, I hope he learns to play for the fun of it, without some coach always yelling at him to get out there and win.

In social and environmental studies, I hope he learns to look critically at the society around him, to compare the role it offers him with the one it offers the girl who sits beside him and ask Why? I hope he learns to see the family as a basic unit in society, but one which is capable of infinite variety and change, just as the people who compose it are.

I hope he learns, too, that he lives on a very, very small planet, that he is one human being among billions, who, in turn, are only one species among millions and that his survival depends on his seeing this fact as a matter of *relationship* and not of domination.

In math and science class, I hope he learns that not everything can be quantified, measured, weighed. I hope someone points out to him that our society's belief in "objectivity" is a false one and that even to the so-called "hard sciences" we bring the biases of culture, class, and gender which determine, even when we don't recognize it, how and what we "see."

In every class, I hope he learns to listen to what the girls have to say as carefully as he listens to the other boys. I hope he learns that "conversation" carries within it the meaning of exploring ideas *together*, rather than that of mounting a debate in which only one point of view can "win."

But having gone to school myself, I know, of course, how much is not learned in the classroom, but in the playground, in the parks, on the street. Will there be men around to show him that the rough, aggressive comradeship that men so often employ is not the only way to express affection? I hope there are some to teach him that you can tell someone you love him by hugging him, as easily as by punching him on the arm or playing a practical joke. I also hope that if he worries that such an act might label him as a "sissy" or a "homo," someone will challenge him with "so what?"

And when he learns the insults of the playground, will someone point out to him that calling someone a "fag" is no different than calling someone a "nigger" or a "dago"?

And what about anger? Will there be enough examples besides what he has at home to counterbalance the pressure of a culture which accepts aggression and violence at every level as the only practical means of resolving conflict?

Every parent knows, of course, that there is only so much you can do. After that, you have to trust that you have done a good job. But for women like myself, who are the mothers of sons, this trust is a little harder to come by. Beyond the influence of our home, my son feels the enormous pressure of a culture which has a lot invested in the continuation of a traditional male role, a culture which offers enormous power and privilege to those who accept that limited idea of what it means to be a man.

As I watched my son ride off this morning, I realized that I was entrusting him to a public education system in its widest possible sense. What sort of man he becomes depends not only on his teachers, but also on everyone he meets, on how much they have thought about the roles our culture gives them depending on their sex and on how hard they work at changing those roles. Like every child, my son represents the future, but it's a future that grows out of our present. His limitations or possibilities, the possibilities for all of us, depend on what *we* do, now.

Charles

BY
SHIRLEY
JACKSON

The day my son Laurie started kindergarten he renounced corduroy overalls with bibs and began wearing blue jeans with a belt; I watched him go off the first morning with the older girl next door, seeing clearly that an era of my life was ended, my sweet-voiced nursery-school tot replaced by a long-trousered, swaggering character who forgot to stop at the corner and wave good-bye to me.

He came home the same way, the front door slamming open, his cap on the floor, and the voice suddenly became raucous shouting, "Isn't anybody *here*?"

At lunch he spoke insolently to his father, spilled his baby sister's milk, and remarked that his teacher said we were not to take the name of the Lord in vain.

"How *was* school today?" I asked, elaborately casual.

"All right," he said.

"Did you learn anything?" his father asked.

Laurie regarded his father coldly. "I didn't learn nothing," he said.

"Anything," I said. "Didn't learn anything."

"The teacher spanked a boy, though," Laurie said, addressing his bread and butter. "For being fresh," he added, with his mouth full.

"What did he do?" I asked. "Who was it?"

Laurie thought. "It was Charles," he said. "He was fresh. The teacher spanked him and made him stand in a corner. He was awfully fresh."

"What did he do?" I asked again, but Laurie slid off his chair, took a cookie and left, while his father was still saying, "See here, young man."

The next day Laurie remarked at lunch, as soon as he sat down, "Well, Charles was bad again today." He grinned enormously and said, "Today Charles hit the teacher."

"Good heavens," I said, mindful of the Lord's name, "I suppose he got spanked again?"

"He sure did," Laurie said. "Look up," he said to his father.

"What?" his father said, looking up.

"Look down," Laurie said. "Look at my thumb. Gee, you're dumb." He began to laugh insanely.

"Why did Charles hit the teacher?" I asked quickly.

"Because she tried to make him color with red crayons," Laurie said. "Charles wanted to color with green crayons so he hit the teacher and she spanked him and said nobody play with Charles but everybody did."

The third day—it was Wednesday of the first week—Charles bounced a see-saw onto the head of a little girl and made her bleed, and the teacher made him stay inside all during recess. Thursday Charles had to stand in a corner during story-time because he kept pounding his feet on the floor. Friday Charles was deprived of blackboard privileges because he threw chalk.

On Saturday I remarked to my husband, "Do you think kindergarten is too unsettling for Laurie? All this toughness, and bad grammar, and this Charles boy sounds like such a bad influence."

"It'll be all right," my husband said reassuringly. "Bound to be people like Charles in the world. Might as well meet them now as later."

On Monday Laurie came home late, full of news. "Charles," he shouted as he came up the hill; I was waiting anxiously on the front steps. "Charles," Laurie yelled all the way up the hill. "Charles was bad again."

"Come right in," I said, as soon as he came close enough. "Lunch is waiting."

"You know what Charles did?" he demanded, following me through the door. "Charles yelled so in school they sent a boy in from first grade to tell the teacher she had to make Charles keep quiet, and so Charles had to stay after school. And so all the children stayed to watch him."

"What did he do?" I asked.

"He just sat there," Laurie said, climbing into his chair at the table. "Hi, Pop, y'old dust mop."

"Charles had to stay after school today," I told my husband. "Everyone stayed with him."

"What does this Charles look like?" my husband asked Laurie. "What's his other name?"

"He's bigger than me," Laurie said, "And he doesn't have any rubbers and he doesn't ever wear a jacket."

Monday night was the first Parent-Teachers meeting, and only the fact that the baby had a cold kept me from going; I wanted passionately to meet Charles's mother. On Tuesday Laurie remarked suddenly, "Our teacher had a friend come see her in school today."

"Charles's mother?" my husband and I asked simultaneously.

"Naaah," Laurie said scornfully. "It was a man who came and made us do exercises, we had to touch our toes. Look." He climbed down from his chair and squatted down and touched his toes. "Like this," he said. He got solemnly back into his chair and said, picking up his fork, "Charles didn't even do exercises."

"That's fine," I said heartily. "Didn't Charles want to do exercises?"

"Naaah," Laurie said. "Charles was so fresh to the teacher's friend he wasn't *let* do exercises."

"Fresh again?" I said.

"He kicked the teacher's friend," Laurie said. "The teacher's friend told Charles to touch his toes like I just did and Charles kicked him."

"What are they going to do about Charles, do you suppose?" Laurie's father asked him.

Laurie shrugged elaborately. "Throw him out of school, I guess," he said.

Wednesday and Thursday were routine; Charles yelled during story hour and hit a boy in the stomach and made him cry. On Friday Charles stayed after school again and so did all the other children.

With the third week of kindergarten Charles was an institution in our family; the baby was being a Charles when she cried all afternoon;

Laurie did a Charles when he filled his wagon full of mud and pulled it through the kitchen; even my husband, when he caught his elbow in the telephone cord and pulled telephone, ashtray and a bowl of flowers off the table, said, after the first minutes, "Looks like Charles."

During the third and fourth weeks it looked like a reformation in Charles; Laurie reported grimly at lunch on Thursday of the third week, "Charles was so good today the teacher gave him an apple."

"What?" I said, and my husband added warily, "You mean Charles?"

"Charles," Laurie said. "He gave the crayons around and he picked up the books afterward and the teacher said he was her helper."

"What happened?" I asked incredulously.

"He was her helper, that's all," Laurie said, and shrugged.

"Can this be true, about Charles?" I asked my husband that night. "Can something like this happen?"

"Wait and see," my husband said cynically. "When you've got a Charles to deal with, this may mean he's only plotting."

He seemed to be wrong. For over a week Charles was the teacher's helper; each day he handed things out and he picked things up; no one had to stay after school.

"The P.T.A. meeting's next week again," I told my husband one evening. "I'm going to find Charles's mother there."

"Ask her what happened to Charles," my husband said. "I'd like to know."

"I'd like to know myself," I said.

On Friday of that week things were back to normal. "You know what Charles did today?" Laurie demanded at the lunch table, in a voice slightly awed. "He told a little girl to say a word and she said it and the teacher washed her mouth out with soap and Charles laughed."

"What word?" his father asked unwisely, and Laurie said, "I'll have to whisper it to you, it's so bad." He got down off his chair and went around to his father. His father bent his head down and Laurie whispered joyfully. His father's eyes widened.

"Did Charles tell the little girl to say *that*?" he asked respectfully.

"She said it *twice*," Laurie said. "Charles told her to say it *twice*."

"What happened to Charles?" my husband asked.

"Nothing," Laurie said. "He was passing out the crayons."

Monday morning Charles abandoned the little girl and said the evil word himself three or four times, getting his mouth washed out with soap each time. He also threw chalk.

My husband came to the door with me that evening as I set out for the P.T.A. meeting. "Invite her over for a cup of tea after the meeting," he said. "I want to get a look at her."

"If only she's there," I said prayerfully.

"She'll be there," my husband said. "I don't see how they could hold a P.T.A. meeting without Charles's mother."

At the meeting I sat restlessly, scanning each comfortable matronly face, trying to determine which one hid the secret of Charles. None of them looked to me haggard enough. No one stood up in the meeting and apologized for the way her son had been acting. No one mentioned Charles.

After the meeting I identified and sought out Laurie's kindergarten teacher. She had a plate with a cup of tea and a piece of chocolate cake; I had a plate with a cup of tea and a piece of marshmallow cake. We maneuvered up to one another cautiously, and smiled.

"I've been so anxious to meet you," I said. "I'm Laurie's mother."

"We're all so interested in Laurie," she said.

"Well, he certainly likes kindergarten," I said. "He talks about it all the time."

"We had a little trouble adjusting, the first week or so," she said primly, "but now he's a fine little helper. With occasional lapses, of course."

"Laurie usually adjusts very quickly," I said. "I suppose this time it's Charles's influence."

"Charles?"

"Yes," I said, laughing, "you must have your hands full in that kindergarten, with Charles."

"Charles?" she said. "We don't have any Charles in the kindergarten."

from

Invisible
Friends

~

BY

ALAN

AYCKBOURN

Invisible Friends *is the story of Lucy, a teenage girl who can't seem to connect with her mother, father, or impossible brother. Zara is Lucy's "invisible friend" who becomes annoyingly visible before the play goes very far. In this speech, Lucy introduces us to the still invisible Zara.*

Lucy: [(*As she goes upstairs, to audience*)] Come with me, if you will. Upstairs. If you listen very carefully you can just hear the distant sounds of the greater spotted Grisly Gary, my unbelievably talkative brother. Grisly Gary is doing a building course at the technical college, training to be a bucket.
(*She reaches the door of Gary's room. The music is louder now.*) Here we go. I'll just have a quiet word with him. Cover your ears. (*Lucy opens Gary's door. The heavy-metal music comes up to a deafening level. Lucy, when she speaks, is quite inaudible. [Gary, lying on the bed with his eyes closed, fails to notice her at all.]*)
(*Mouthing, swiftly*) Hallo, Grisly. It's your loving sister, Lucy. Just to tell you I've been picked for the school swimming team. Thought

you'd like to know. Bye, Grisly. *(**Lucy** closes the door again. The music goes down to a lower level.)* I enjoyed that chat. *(She opens the door of her own room and goes inside.)* This is my room. No one's allowed in here, except me. I'm a very tidy sort of person. Which is a bit extraordinary in this house. I think I must be a freak. I actually like to know where I've put things. This is my bed. That's my desk. And up there on the shelf. Those are my special, most favourite books. *(The music pounds through the wall.)* Actually, one of the reasons I keep it tidy is because my very, very best friend, Zara, also likes things tidy. Oh, yes, I ought to explain to you about Zara. You may have heard my mum talking about my invisible friend. Do you remember? Well, that's my invisible friend, Zara. *(Introducing her.)* This is Zara. I want you to meet Zara. Zara, say hallo. That's it. Will you say hallo to Zara, my invisible friend? I invented Zara—oh, years ago—when I was seven or eight. Just for fun. I think I was ill at that time and wasn't allowed to play with any of my real friends, so I made up Zara. She's my special friend that no one can see except me. Of course, I can't really see her either. Not really. Although sometimes I...it's almost as if I could see her, sometimes. If I concentrate very hard it's like I can just glimpse her out of the corner of my eye. *(She is thoughtful for a second.)* Still. Anyway. I've kept Zara for years and years. Until they all started saying I was much too old for that sort of thing and got worried and started talking about sending for a doctor. So then I didn't take her round with me quite so much after that. But she's still here. And when I feel really sad and depressed like I do today, then I sit and talk to Zara. Zara always understands. Zara always listens. She's special. Aren't you, Zara? *(She listens to Zara.)* What's that? Yes, I wish he'd turn his music down, too. I've asked him, haven't I? *(Mimicking Gary)* 'How can I hear it if I turn it down, I can't hear the bass then, can I?' I used to have pictures in here but every time he put a disc on they fell off the walls. *(Pause. The music continues.)* I mean, don't get me wrong. We like loud music, don't we Zara? We love loud music. Sometimes. *(Yelling)* BUT NOT ALL THE TIME. *(Pause.)* Why doesn't he ever listen to quiet music? Just once. Wouldn't that be nice? *(The music changes to a delicate piece of Bach, just for a second. [**Gary** sits up in an attitude of deep appreciation, eyes still closed. Then the music resumes as before and he lies back down again.])* But if he did that, he wouldn't be Grisly Gary then, would he? (Pause.) Oh, Zara, did I tell you I've been picked for the school swimming team? Isn't that exciting? Yes. Thank you. I'm glad you're excited, too. Good. *(Pause) (Shouting)* IF ANYONE IS INTERESTED AT ALL, I WAS PICKED FOR THE SCHOOL SWIMMING TEAM TODAY. WHAT ABOUT THAT, FOLKS? *(She listens. No reply.)* Great. Thanks for your support, everyone. *(Tearful)* They might at least...They could have at least...Oh, Zara...I know you're always here, but sometimes I get so...lonely... *(She sits on her bed, sad, angry and frustrated.)*

The
Accident

~

BY

JOYCE

MARSHALL

In that last and most difficult of our three summers in the village, I see us trailing around endlessly together in a little string. I can almost look down and find those children, purely, without the future—all I now know or surmise about Hilary and Laura and have learned or made of myself. I would like to really get back to them, just as they were, because then perhaps I could untangle the truth of what happened or just seemed to happen—events or fancies that are linked for me always with the picture of three children moving along unwillingly and rather slowly, never side by side as I remember them but one after one after one in the distinct shapes and sizes that spaced out the five years. We were two and a half years apart, so precisely that Laura, the youngest, shared my birthday. Which was just one of many things I held against her.

The youngest except for the baby. I should make that clear. The baby, not yet called Claudia because my parents were finding it harder even than usual to agree upon a name, was never a threat. The real warfare was between us older three. And it was warfare. It was relentless. It was bitter. Yet at the time I speak of, before we were strong enough to break away (physically) from one another, we were tied together most of the day. For safety. We lived—or camped—that summer a long way back from the broadening of the St. Lawrence River we called the lake on the dirt and pebble trail known somewhat grandly as St. John's Road; for the twice-daily swims that were ritual in our family we had to cross two sets of railway tracks—each with its little station, gate and roller-coaster hill—and later the main village street across to the lake side and the beginning of the gentle curve that led around to the beach.

In winter I had all the aloneness I could wish in my own class at school. And different fears and different learning. But memory is capricious. I seldom, when I look back at my childhood, connect the seasons, as if our twice-yearly upheavals of dogs and cats and children split them apart. And when I think of the struggle with my sisters, I remember chiefly the summers, which were long in our family, slow similar days stretching from May until November. And, of course, the road—that soft easy curve edging the lake. Is it still there, I wonder. Or has it been swallowed up by the airport? I have never tried to know which. It remains. My archetypal road that I dream of again and again in so many ways. I was there again last night but the lake had become an abyss, I was trying to throw an infant—a very large screaming infant—over the side; I woke in panic in what seemed an immense and hollow room. And, because I dislike those murderous dreams, which I shouldn't need any more, I began to think instead of that other safer terror, the accident, and to ask myself, as I have done so many times, whether it really happened as I seem to remember it. Did the man exist, in fact? Can it be possible that I was allowed to stand so close to him, leaning right over him as I seem to do, listening to words that like so many of my childhood words I have no means to understand? He seems real. At least the fear and horror do. Perhaps I have reached back to imagine him, harbinger. At times I can believe this and yet I do seem to see him clearly, lying there bleeding on the edge of that vanished road.

I was nine that year. This I am sure of because the sister who would not become Claudia till ten minutes or so before our grandfather, alarming in canonical robes, splashed her with water and uttered the name, was still quite new. When I see the man, I see her also, lying in her crouched baby position in our old straw carriage with its corduroy lining, under one of the trees in the bumpy ungrassed yard of that strange house. The first human being I loved. The emotion we feel for parents is a demanding, seeking. This new kind of love, which I found whole in the moment the new little creature was laid on my arms, was a huge inner swelling almost cracking my ribs. Now I understand, I remember thinking, what they mean when they say: My heart swelled. A peremptory feeling, inexplicable, a bit frightening. I didn't know what I was going to do with it. But I rather liked it. It was magic. It still seems magic as I recall it. No later love has staled that first.

I tried to spend as much time as I could beside the baby. Serve her. Just look at her. I ran and fetched. Kept lifting the green mosquito netting tacked over her carriage for a new careful study of the always astonishing line of the cheek, tiny token fingers, bluish eyelid shells. I told myself I would die for her, this small human I didn't have to try to please, who could do nothing for me. My mother, who was almost instinctively alarmed, or at least troubled, by my behavior a great part of the time, used to thrust me away when I poked my head too close as she changed or nursed the baby. Why when she was so busy was I suddenly always under her feet? Why was I so quiet? Why didn't I go and help Hilary who was trying to teach Laura to skip hot pepper on the bit of level road in front of the house? Why didn't I have friends? (When she knew as well as I did that in this rickety farmhouse way back from the village and its few summer cottages there were no friends for me to have.)

I have called it a difficult summer. This was partly the house, not enough rooms for us and those too small, awkwardly cut up and confining with its little low windows and evil smells, the presence of the farm's real owners in a shack at the end of the vegetable garden just back of the house. My parents, who were always slow about summer rentals, had taken the place at night, had not realized that the quarters to which the farm-family proposed to move for the summer were so close. It was disconcerting to have them all there weeding by day almost under our kitchen window and at night sitting in a row in front of their shack, rocking in unison, gazing at us. My mother, who was sociable, tried waving and gesticulating but, though they smiled and nodded always, it went no further; clearly they had a strong sense of bounds and when our dog went too close they shooed him back. There was quite a large family of half-grown children, including a girl of about my age.

"Go and play with her, Martha," my mother said to me once.

THE ACCIDENT : **17**

"Maybe she'd like to. Poor little thing. Always working. She could help you with French. Show you the cows and chickens. Even if you can't talk much, you could…skip, play hopscotch."

The thought of approaching that thin fierce-looking dark girl, whose bed I perhaps slept in and who must hate me for it as I would have hated her in a similar case, filled me with terror but, because I didn't want to admit—and defend—my cowardice, I just said crossly that I didn't like her.

"Yes, she does look a bit common," my mother said.

Her answer, which should have made my not liking the girl all right, was merely puzzling. Did it mean that we were uncommon? And if so, why and how? I knew there was no use trying to find out. My mother was in a very bad mood, tied down almost all day in this poky house where diapers had to be boiled in pails on a wood-burning stove and spread over bushes and rocks to dry. She couldn't play tennis and seldom found time to wheel the carriage to the beach. No days could suddenly be declared too hot for anything but a picnic by the lake or a wild ramble across fields to find blueberries. My father was interested that year, I think, in a mining property in northern Ontario. He was away much of the time, not coming home at night to cool and calm us, change the atmosphere, sing us grand opera, substitute his sort of energy for our mother's. There wasn't even a maid to talk to. The one we'd brought with us had taken one sniff at the kitchen and, refusing even to be led up to examine "the dear little room under the eaves" where she was to sleep, demanded to be put on the very next train back to Montreal. (Our maids often left abruptly. I can't remember even one who lasted a whole summer. We liked the maids, who had fascinating lives and discussed them with us.)

My mother couldn't understand, she kept saying with one of the sideways looks that seemed to discover us for the first time, why she had let this happen. "Why did I marry and have four children?" she asked again and again as if sooner or later she'd find a reason. "I should have been a business girl." We must take a lesson from her and all be business girls. She would see to this herself. I can't remember whether we answered. Mother often complained and in a very vocal, almost automatic way. I don't think we minded being lumped together as something deplorable she had permitted to happen to her one day when she was looking the wrong way. We were very solidly here; that was all that mattered. Our mother was quick and restless, her energies loose and untapped. In another time and place she would have been a magnificent suffragette. No force-feeding her. She would have starved to the death, no question about that. And whenever I read about Emmeline Pankhurst I see the red-gold hair, proud mouth and glinting eyes of my mother. Meanwhile we were all to be business girls, remote as that seemed. This summer we had other concerns.

The family was shifting again. I can say again, though this is the first of the shifts I really remember. We had always quarrelled, we three, sometimes savagely and physically, had fought as children have to do for position and space, had worked out certain niches for ourselves. Now there was a fourth and places no longer held. Not that we were aware of any of this except in some deep domain of blood and bone. We knew simply—at least I knew—that it was a difficult summer, hot, monotonous. This was my first experience of boredom; I hadn't known that days could simply go on and on, always very much the same. I recall them as hot and parched with a sound of rustling—from the corn perhaps, that rather spindly corn the farm-family weeded. Seldom raining but very often thundery. And no sight or sound or even smell of water. (We were water-creatures in our family, my father too. He had met my mother, we knew, in this very lake, had fallen in love with her sparkling face under the pompommed bathing-cap. We children were all carried into the water before we could walk. And to be in the country but dry, on a hill-top, with no liquid shimmer visible between trees to us was anguish.) And there my mother must stay most of the time with the occasional company of three bickering children who could seldom succeed in being what she frequently told us we ought to be, three dear little sisters. (She herself had been one of seven dear little sisters. We had seen their picture, standing in a close loving rank in front of our grandfather's old rectory at Bolton Centre, all very shiny and neat in high-necked dresses with a great many tucks. They were our despair. They had loved one another then and were still the best of friends, greeting one another after weeks with cries of delight. Children who grew up in rectories were different, it seemed to me, loved automatically, big ones liked nothing better than taking care of little ones, no one ever bit her sister. I could never live up to them.)

I was skinny and long at nine, all knobs and angles. I did not find myself appealing, could not make myself look pretty even with constant practice at the mirror. Worse, my behavior never came out quite as I wanted it to. Success in childhood, I see now, depends in large part on one's gifts as a mimic. I had none. And as I could seldom think quickly enough of a handy lie, I was obliged to try to say what I meant—and sound foolish. Hilary was an excellent mimic, stood watchful close to the grownups and learned to be charming. She was the chief of my enemies, the first usurper, rooting me out of a place I possessed and must long for still. (So that I murder her still in dreams. I'm sorry, Hilary. It's a very impersonal murder.) Not till recently did it occur to me that I was also chief of Hilary's enemies, already firmly established when she came. So that she could only become my mirror? Was obliged to be good, docile and positive because I wasn't. Did I make Hilary too in part as I struggled to make myself? I can see her trotting about that summer, more docile than ever, helping and serving, busying herself with the sort of games adults find enchanting—tucked in some little corner playing house or teacher, dressing up the cat, cuddling Laura.

For Laura, that untested child, had turned fretful, Laura for whom everything had always come so easily simply because she was beautiful, in the creamy dimpled way that is the only way for children to be beautiful, and with two expressions: a touching gravity, a beguiling smile. It was hard not to hate someone who just needed to exist to delight. What Hilary thought of her I do not know; this summer she had attached herself to Laura, crooned, protected, made beds for her out of chairs, pretended to feed her. I pinched, crowded, snatched. And Laura, who seldom cried, had never told tales, not even when a blow from my croquet mallet made her bite her tongue till it bled, was now always whimpering, saw threats in shadows, screamed at thunder so that she had to be taken out of bed, rocked, called darling baby. She was called darling baby far too often, I thought. Beguiling always, she was now, it seemed to me, learning to work at being beguiling. I resented this bitterly, wanting my treasure, the real baby, to have all the love, simply because she was my chosen one. I noticed that Laura seldom looked at the baby, didn't seem even to like her. Jealous for my darling, I saw any subtraction of love from her as an insult to me. It was a trying summer as we slowly became more and more ourselves and in new ways. If it was really quite that simple. I can't be sure because, when you get down to it, I remember very little. Just a general stormy sense—that rustle, all that growly thunder—an impression of pushing and pulling, of things that ought to be clear and easy not clear or easy.

And though I would have preferred to stay at home with my darling, who was learning to smile when I lifted the netting to examine her, I was obliged to spend almost all those long summer days with two enemies. Walking with them through that village where no one ever spoke to us. Fairly well used, I suppose—and this may be a handy lesson to learn early—to a world in which many things and most people were indifferent. In the city during the winter I sometimes joined with my schoolmates to throw stones at the French children. *Pea soup. Pea soup and Johnny cake make the Frenchie's belly ache.* I had learned these interesting taunts while I was learning "Come over, red rover" and "One two three alarie," and all were games, I thought. In this very small village, which I recall as silent, almost painted because nothing I heard was comprehended, in some way so subtle and yet so clear I never tried to examine it, I was very definitely not at home. It must have been at about this time that I began to feel rather precarious, that finger and thumb could flick me away. (Even when I was running, pelting through fields, and should have felt most physical and real, I would begin to seem weightless, floaty.) But if we did not seem to be observed, except with some loose blanket disapproval—so much the same, always, it could be pretty well ignored—this had its good side too. We could go anywhere we liked. In a world where all the adults were enemies, leagued together by similar tastes and standards, it was a relief to find some who, however great their displeasure, would never tell our parents.

When I say we could go anywhere, I don't mean by this that there was anywhere much to go. We weren't given pocket-money, couldn't have kept track of it in our clutter of sand-pails, wadded towels, and rubber bathing-caps, and so couldn't go into the store—except on occasional Saturdays with my father—to brood over the huge glass jars that held all the marvellous candy that could be bought for a single cent. But because we were all irritable that summer we broke rules, almost without thinking. There weren't many. *Don't loiter or peer into the stores.* We loitered and peered. *Don't climb fences on St. John's Road. You might meet a bull.* We climbed fences and picked flowers almost out of the mouths of the cows, examined bluebirds' nests in rotting fence-posts, pulled lone stalks of timothy to suck. And when there was a little gathering of people in the expanded sidewalk in front of the grocery-store or the butcher's, we walked right into it, trailed through it and, as it seemed, made no more impression than when we chopped through the water with our bouncing and energetic breast-stroke at our little cove. Which is why, I imagine, we could have managed, young and small as we were, to get through to the front of the crowd that pressed that day around the man who lay dying after the accident. The village people simply didn't notice us, small alien figures always roaming about.

I've thought of it all so many times, smudging it probably. But always the same details come. And the same gaps. We were on our way home from the beach, had passed the long fence of the magnificent house, fancily gabled behind trees—it had fifty-six rooms, I'd heard—and there just ahead were all those people staring at something in front of them. I suppose to us it was simply an interesting sight. We were curious. So in we went, I first because bigger and stronger, better at wriggling through, the others after.

There were often accidents at the sharp bend the road was forced to take before it slipped into its slow curve. On the north side, the side where we weren't allowed to walk, the corner of a white-plastered, rather small house jutted through the sidewalk a foot or two into the road. Some old witch-lady had lived there for years, refusing to sacrifice part of her house or let it be moved back. She believed, we had heard, that since she and her house had been there when the road was just a track, they had a right to remain. Cars often met head-on at that spot. The man in today's accident, I learned from adult discussion later, had been speeding, had been drunk, might have fallen asleep in the sun, at any rate had failed to make the sudden veer. His car was on our side of the road, against a telephone pole, he himself a few feet away. Someone must have moved him for I see him as lying straight and tidy on his back, on the grassy strip between the wooden sidewalk and the unrailed gallery of a house. The village people looked down at him as if, having done what they could, the necessary phone calls made, they sensed that he wanted to be alone and let him be. I have an impression of tremendous excitement and yet silence. He himself was not silent. He was crying as I looked into his face, very close to it, bent a little forward as I had had to do to work my way through the crowd. He was calling someone, at least speaking the same few syllables again and again. I think I imagined that he was calling a name. Have I added the blood? Transported that broken bleeding face from elsewhere? Normandy? Spain? I remember a great deal of blood, all very red. In his hair, running into his eyes. Perhaps coming from his eyes. (I seem to know that he couldn't see.) A red pool in the grass around his head as he went on calling in that very fast, bubbling sort of voice. I believe I simply stood there, stooping slightly, looking at him. Not wanting to. Unable to turn or move.

Then at some point an awareness of Laura. Right at my knee. Perhaps pulling at me, for I remember her hand, her battered yellow sand-pail and the little shovel with the paintless handle. (This must be real for I see her hand in the scale of those times, the top of her head with the glint of the sun on its crown.) She was behind me, trying to get past me, whimpering, frightened. (I asked her once, "Do you remember, Laura? A terrible accident—a man badly hurt when we were little?" "Oh yes," she said. "At one of those parades Dad used to take us to. A horse reared and fell back, crushing the rider." And looked so stricken, for Laura has grown up to be the most tender-hearted of us all, that I pressed no further. We lived different lives, our memories are loose in our own heads and seldom meet.) Hilary I haven't asked, for Hilary would maintain as she always does that she remembers nothing at all from before she was eight. Yet very clearly at my other side I can hear her high-pitched, very positive voice: "They're going to take him to the hospital and they're going to sew him all together again. Don't worry, Laura. They're going to—."

"Shut-up," my own voice, "oh shut up." And I looked down—again or still—at Laura's face just at my side, saw it for the first time as a human face detached from me, crumpling before something far too big for it. Saw all sorts of other things, whether or not I put them in words, and with that first sense of the true otherness of others just as themselves, had an inkling at least of all that would be required of me, willing or not, as I went on living—demands that are made of us that we must fulfil and love that can come, and does, in all sorts of forms, not only for the chosen.

I think I knew I had to get Laura away from there and did, took hold of that hand with the sand-pail and, twisting and turning as I had entered it, led her out of the crowd. But very little is sure in our memories. Of all our trudges home through the village, our walks up St. John's Road, I cannot select that one from the others. It was a difficult and edgy summer. Always thundery, always very much the same.

The Fisherman

~

BY

RICHARD

SOMMER

Still there is a photograph of me
crouched against the railings of a bridge
watching my father make a mess of casting
a brilliant fly into the bushes.

My father tried fly-fishing because all
the men who were good at it smoked pipes.

My father smoked a pipe because the men
who liked pipes were good at fly-casting.

I remember the thrust of my face against
the cool railings, tilted down at the stream
or drawn back, watching my father.

I remember also that my father didn't
catch anything although his tacklebox
had everything already in it.

If my father were still living, I think
I would take him in my arms and kiss him
and tell him that it didn't matter.

But that is easier to say because
he is dead and I don't have to do it.

I still don't know who took the picture
of the railings, of me, of my father's legs.

It probably wasn't my mother.

To Every Thing There Is a Season

BY

ALISTAIR

MACLEOD

am speaking here of a time when I was eleven and lived with my
family on our small farm on the west coast of Cape Breton. My
family had been there for a long, long time and so it seemed had
I. And much of that time seems like the proverbial yesterday. Yet when
I speak on this Christmas 1977, I am not sure how much I speak with
the voice of that time or how much in the voice of what I have since
become. And I am not sure how many liberties I may be taking with
the boy I think I was. For Christmas is a time of both past and present
and often the two are imperfectly blended. As we step into its
nowness we often look behind.

We have been waiting now, it seems, forever. Actually, it has been
most intense since Halloween when the first snow fell upon us as we
moved like muffled mummers upon darkened country roads. The large
flakes were soft and new then and almost generous and the earth to
which they fell was still warm and as yet unfrozen. They fell in silence
into the puddles and into the sea where they disappeared at the
moment of contact. They disappeared, too, upon touching the heated
redness of our necks and hands or the faces of those who did not wear

masks. We carried our pillowcases from house to house, knocking on doors to become silhouettes in the light thrown out from kitchens (white pillowcases held out by whitened forms). The snow fell between us and the doors and was transformed in shimmering golden beams. When we turned to leave, it fell upon our footprints and as the night wore on obliterated them and all the records of our movements. In the morning everything was soft and still and November had come upon us.

My brother Kenneth, who is two and a half, is unsure of his last Christmas. It is Halloween that looms largest in his memory as an exceptional time of being up late in magic darkness and falling snow. "Who are you going to dress up as at Christmas?" he asks. "I think I'll be a snowman." All of us laugh at that and tell him Santa Claus will find him if he is good and that he need not dress up at all. We go about our appointed tasks waiting for it to happen.

I am troubled myself about the nature of Santa Claus and I am trying to hang on to him in any way that I can. It is true that at my age I no longer *really* believe in him yet I have hoped in all his possibilities as fiercely as I can; much in the same way, I think, that the drowning man waves desperately to the lights of the passing ship on the high sea's darkness. For without him, as without the man's ship, it seems our fragile lives would be so much more desperate.

My mother has been fairly tolerant of my attempted perpetuation. Perhaps because she has encountered it before. Once I overheard her speaking about my sister Anne to one of her neighbours. "I thought Anne would *believe* forever," she said. "I practically had to tell her." I have somehow always wished I had not heard her say that as I seek sanctuary and reinforcement even in an ignorance I know I dare not trust.

Kenneth, however, believes with an unadulterated fervour, and so do Bruce and Barry who are six-year-old twins. Beyond me there is Anne who is thirteen and Mary who is fifteen, both of whom seem to be leaving childhood at an alarming rate. My mother has told us that she was already married when she was seventeen, which is only two years older than Mary is now. That too seems strange to contemplate and perhaps childhood is shorter for some than it is for others. I think of this sometimes in the evenings when we have finished our chores and the supper dishes have been cleared away and we are supposed to be doing our homework. I glance sideways at my mother, who is always knitting or mending, and at my father, who mostly sits by the stove coughing quietly with his handkerchief at his mouth. He has "not been well" for over two years and has difficulty breathing whenever he moves at more than the slowest pace. He is most sympathetic of all concerning my extended hopes and says we should hang on to the good things in our lives as long as we are able. As I look at him out of the corner of my eye, it does not seem that he has many of them left. He is old, we think, at forty-two.

Yet Christmas, in spite of all the doubts of our different ages, is a fine and splendid time, and now as we pass the midpoint of December our expectations are heightened by the increasing coldness that has settled down upon us. The ocean is flat and calm and along the coast, in the scooped-out coves, has turned to an icy slush. The brook that flows past our house is almost totally frozen and there is only a small channel of rushing water that flows openly at its very centre. When we let the cattle out to drink, we chop holes with the axe at the brook's edge so that they can drink without venturing onto the ice.

The sheep move in and out of their lean-to shelter restlessly stamping their feet or huddling together in tightly packed groups. A conspiracy of wool against the cold. The hens perch high on their roosts with their feathers fluffed out about them, hardly feeling it worthwhile to descend to the floor for their few scant kernels of grain. The pig, who has little time before his butchering, squeals his displeasure to the cold and with his snout tosses his wooden trough high in the icy air. The splendid young horse paws the planking of his stall and gnaws the wooden cribwork of his manger.

We have put a protective barricade of spruce boughs about our kitchen door and banked our house with additional boughs and billows of eel grass. Still, the pail of water we leave standing in the porch is solid in the morning and has to be broken with the hammer. The clothes my mother hangs on the line are frozen almost instantly and sway and creak from their suspending clothespins like sections of dismantled robots: the stiff-legged rasping trousers and the shirts and sweaters with unyielding arms outstretched. In the morning we race from our frigid upstairs bedrooms to finish dressing around the kitchen stove.

We would extend our coldness half a continent away to the Great Lakes of Ontario so that it might hasten the Christmas coming of my oldest brother, Neil. He is nineteen and employed on the "lake boats," the long flat carriers of grain and iron ore whose season ends any day after December 10, depending on the ice conditions. We wish it to be cold, cold on the Great Lakes of Ontario, so that he may come home to us as soon as possible. Already his cartons have arrived. They come from different places: Cobourg, Toronto, St. Catharines, Welland, Windsor, Sarnia, Sault Ste. Marie. Places that we, with the exception of my father, have never been. We locate them excitedly on the map, tracing their outlines with eager fingers. The cartons bear the lettering of Canada Steamship Lines, and are bound with rope knotted intricately in the fashion of sailors. My mother says they contain his "clothes" and we are not allowed to open them.

For us it is impossible to know the time or manner of his coming. If the lakes freeze early, he may come by train because it is cheaper. If the lakes stay open until December 20, he will have to fly because his time will be more precious than his money. He will hitchhike the last sixty or hundred miles from either station or airport. On our part, we can do nothing but listen with straining ears to radio reports of distant ice formations. His coming seems to depend on so many factors which are out there far beyond us and over which we lack control.

The days go by in fevered slowness until finally on the morning of December 23 the strange car rolls into our yard. My mother touches her hand to her lips and whispers "Thank God." My father gets up unsteadily from his chair to look through the window. Their longed-for son and our golden older brother is here at last. He is here with his reddish hair and beard and we can hear his hearty laugh. He will be happy and strong and confident for us all.

There are three other young men with him who look much the same as he. They too are from the boats and are trying to get home to Newfoundland. They must still drive a hundred miles to reach the ferry at North Sydney. The car seems very old. They purchased it in Thorold for two hundred dollars because they were too late to make any reservations, and they have driven steadily since they began. In northern New Brunswick their windshield wipers failed but instead of stopping they tied lengths of cord to the wipers' arms and passed them through the front window vents. Since that time, in whatever precipitation, one of them has pulled the cords back and forth to make the wipers function. This information falls tiredly but excitedly from their lips and we greedily gather it in. My father pours them drinks of rum and my mother takes out her mincemeat and the fruitcakes she has been carefully hoarding. We lean on the furniture or look from the safety of sheltered doorways. We would like to hug our brother but are too shy with strangers present. In the kitchen's warmth, the young men begin to nod and doze, their heads dropping suddenly to their chests. They nudge each other with their feet in an attempt to keep awake. They will not stay and rest because they have come so far and tomorrow is Christmas Eve and stretches of mountains and water still lie between them and those they love.

After they leave we pounce upon our brother physically and verbally. He laughs and shouts and lifts us over his head and swings us in his muscular arms. Yet in spite of his happiness he seems surprised at the appearance of his father whom he has not seen since March. My father merely smiles at him while my mother bites her lip.

Now that he is here there is a great flurry of activity. We have left everything we could until the time he might be with us. Eagerly I show him the fir tree on the hill which I have been watching for months and marvel at how easily he fells it and carries it down the hill. We fall over one another in the excitement of decoration.

He promises that on Christmas Eve he will take us to church in the sleigh behind the splendid horse that until his coming we are all afraid to handle. And on the afternoon of Christmas Eve he shoes the horse, lifting each hoof and rasping it fine and hammering the cherry-red horseshoes into shape upon the anvil. Later he drops them hissingly into the steaming tub of water. My father sits beside him on an overturned pail and tells him what to do. Sometimes we argue with our father, but our brother does everything he says.

That night, bundled in hay and voluminous coats, and with heated stones at our feet, we start upon our journey. Our parents and Kenneth remain at home but all the rest of us go. Before we leave we feed the cattle and sheep and even the pig all that they can possibly eat so that they will be contented on Christmas Eve. Our parents wave to us from the doorway. We go four miles across the mountain road. It is a primitive logging trail and there will be no cars or other vehicles upon it. At first the horse is wild with excitement and lack of exercise and my brother has to stand at the front of the sleigh and lean backwards on the reins. Later he settles down to a trot and still later to a walk as the mountain rises before him. We sing all the Christmas songs we know and watch for the rabbits and foxes scudding across the open patches of snow and listen to the drumming of partridge wings. We are never cold.

When we descend to the country church we tie the horse in a grove of trees where he will be sheltered and not frightened by the many cars. We put a blanket over him and give him oats. At the church door the neighbours shake hands with my bother. "Hello, Neil," they say. "How is your father?"

"Oh," he says, just "Oh."

The church is very beautiful at night with its festooned branches and glowing candles and the booming, joyous sounds that come from the choir loft. We go through the service as if we are mesmerized.

On the way home, although the stones have cooled, we remain happy and warm. We listen to the creak of the leather harness and the hiss of runners on the snow and begin to think of the potentiality of presents. When we are about a mile from home the horse senses his destination and breaks into a trot and then into a confident lope. My brother lets him go and we move across the winter landscape like figures freed from a Christmas card. The snow from the horse's hooves falls about our heads like the whiteness of the stars.

After we have stabled the horse we talk with our parents and eat the meal our mother has prepared. And then I am sleepy and it is time for the younger children to be in bed. But tonight my father says to me, "We would like you to stay up with us a while," and so I stay quietly with the older members of my family.

When all is silent upstairs Neil brings in the cartons that contain his "clothes" and begins to open them. He unties the intricate knots quickly, their whorls falling away before his agile fingers. The boxes are filled with gifts neatly wrapped and bearing tags. The ones for my younger brothers say "from Santa Claus" but mine are not among them anymore, as I know with certainty they will never be again. Yet I am not so much surprised as touched by a pang of loss at being here on the adult side of the world. It is as if I have suddenly moved into another room and heard a door click lastingly behind me. I am jabbed by my own small wound.

But then I look at those before me. I look at my parents drawn together before the Christmas tree. My mother has her hand upon my father's shoulder and he is holding his ever-present handkerchief. I look at my sisters who have crossed this threshold ahead of me and now each day journey farther from the lives they knew as girls. I look at my magic older brother who has come to us this Christmas from half a continent away, bringing everything he has and is. All of them are captured in the tableau of their care.

"Every man moves on," says my father quietly, and I think he speaks of Santa Claus, "but there is no need to grieve. He leaves good things behind."

Gaining Yardage

~

BY

LEO

DANGEL

The word *friend* never came up
between Arlo and me—we're farm neighbors
who hang around together, walk beans,
pick rocks, and sit on the bench
at football games, weighing the assets
of the other side's cheerleaders.
Tonight we lead 48 to 6, so the coach
figures sending us both in is safe.
I intercept an underthrown pass
only because I'm playing the wrong position,
and Arlo is right there to block for me
because he's in the wrong place,
so we gallop up the field, in the clear
until their second-string quarterback
meets us at the five-yard line,
determined to make up for his bad throw.

Arlo misses the block, the guy has me
by the leg and jersey, and going down,
I flip the ball back to Arlo, getting up,
who fumbles, and their quarterback
almost recovers, then bobbles the ball
across the goal line, and our coach,
who told even the guys with good hands
never to mess around with laterals,
must feel his head exploding,
when Arlo and I dive on the ball together
in the end zone and dance and slap
each other on the back.
They give Arlo the touchdown, which rightly
should be mine, but I don't mind,
and I suppose we are friends, and will be,
unless my old man or his decides to move
to another part of the country.

from

Quilters

BY

BARBARA DAMASHEK

AND

MOLLY NEWMAN

In their play, Damashuk and Newman have used the scenic mosaic of a patchwork quilt as their inspiration in creating the life-scenes of a pioneer woman and her six daughters.

Annie: *(To the audience)* My ambition is to become a doctor like my father. I'm my father's girl. My greatest accomplishment was when I was ten years old and was successful in chopping off a chicken's head and then dressing it for a chicken dinner. My mother tries to make me do quilts all the time, but I don't want nothing to do with it. I told her, "Never in my life will I stick my fingers til they bleed." Very definitely. My sister Florry is a real good quilter, I guess. Mother says so all the time. Florry's favorite pattern is the Sunbonnet Sue. Mother taught her how to do applique blocks and since then she's made probably a dozen "Sunbonnet Sue" quilts. You've seen 'em, they're like little dolls turned sideways with big sunbonnets on. Florry makes each one different. *(Annie demonstrates, mimicking Florry.)* In one her little foot is turned this way or that, or she'll give her a little parasol, or turn the hat a little bit. People think they're soooo cute. She made one for everybody in the family, so now there are little "Sunbonnet Sue" quilts all over the house. She made a couple of 'em for her friends, and last Spring, when we all got promoted at school, she presented one to our teacher. I nearly died. And she's still at it. Let me tell you, she's driving me crazy with her "Sunbonnet Sues." So I decided to make one quilt and give it to Florry. Like I said, I'm not such a good quilter as her, but I knew just what I wanted to do with this one. It's real small. Twin bed size. I finished it and put it on her bed this morning, but I don't think she's seen it yet. I guess I done some new things with "Sunbonnet Sue." I call it the "Demise of Sunbonnet Sue." Each little block is different, just like Florry does it. I've got a block of her hanging, another one with a knife in her chest, eaten by a snake, eaten by a frog, struck by lightning, and burned up. I'm sorta proud of it. You should see it... *(A scream from the direction of Florry's bedroom.)* It turned out real good! *(She exits smiling.)*

You Just Don't Understand

~

BY

DEBORAH

TANNEN

It Begins At The Beginning

Even if they grow up in the same neighborhood, on the same block, or
in the same house, girls and boys grow up in different worlds of
words. Others talk to them differently and expect and accept different
ways of talking from them. Most important, children learn how to talk,
how to have conversations, not only from their parents but from their
peers. After all, if their parents have a foreign or regional accent,
children do not emulate it; they learn to speak with the pronunciation
of the region where they grow up. Anthropologists Daniel Maltz and
Ruth Borker summarize research showing that boys and girls have
very different ways of talking to their friends. Although they often play
together, boys and girls spend most of their time playing in same-sex
groups. And, although some of the activities they play at are similar,
their favorite games are different, and their ways of using language in
their games are separated by a world of difference.

Boys tend to play outside, in large groups that are hierarchically
structured. Their groups have a leader who tells others what to do and
how to do it, and resists doing what other boys propose. It is by giving

orders and making them stick that high status is negotiated. Another way boys achieve status is to take center stage by telling stories and jokes, and by sidetracking or challenging the stories and jokes of others. Boys' games have winners and losers and elaborate systems of rules that are frequently the subjects of arguments. Finally, boys are frequently heard to boast of their skill and argue about who is best at what.

Girls, on the other hand, play in small groups or in pairs; the center of a girl's social life is a best friend. Within the group, intimacy is key: Differentiation is measured by relative closeness. In their most frequent games, such as jump rope and hopscotch, everyone gets a turn. Many of their activities (such as playing house) do not have winners or losers. Though some girls are certainly more skilled than others, girls are expected not to boast about it, or show that they think they are better than the others. Girls don't give orders; they express their preferences as suggestions, and suggestions are likely to be accepted. Whereas boys say, "Gimme that!" and "Get outta here!" girls say, "Let's do this," and "How about doing that?" Anything else is put down as "bossy." They don't grab center stage—they don't want it—so they don't challenge each other directly. And much of the time, they simply sit together and talk. Girls are not accustomed to jockeying for status in an obvious way; they are more concerned that they be liked.

Gender differences in ways of talking have been described by researchers observing children as young as three. Amy Sheldon videotaped three- to four-year-old boys and girls playing in threesomes at a day-care center. She compared two groups of three—one of boys, one of girls—that got into fights about the same play item: a plastic pickle. Though both groups fought over the same thing, the dynamics by which they negotiated their conflicts were different. In addition to illustrating some of the patterns I have just described, Sheldon's study also demonstrates the complexity of these dynamics.

While playing in the kitchen area of the day-care center, a little girl named Sue wanted the pickle that Mary had, so she argued that Mary should give it up because Lisa, the third girl, wanted it. This led to a conflict about how to satisfy Lisa's (invented) need. Mary proposed a compromise, but Sue protested:

> MARY: I cut it in half. One for Lisa, one for me, one for me.
> SUE: But, Lisa wants a *whole* pickle!

Mary comes up with another creative compromise, which Sue also rejects:

> MARY: Well, it's a whole *half* pickle.
> SUE: No, it isn't.
> MARY: Yes, it is, a whole *half* pickle.
> SUE: *I'll* give her a whole half. I'll give her a *whole whole*. I gave her a whole one.

At this point, Lisa withdraws from the alliance with Sue, who satisfies herself by saying, "I'm pretending I gave you one."

On another occasion, Sheldon videotaped three boys playing in the same kitchen play area, and they too got into a fight about the plastic pickle. When Nick saw that Kevin had the pickle, he demanded it for himself:

> NICK: [Screams] Kevin, but the, oh, I *have* to cut! I want to cut it! It's mine!

Like Sue, Nick involved the third child in his effort to get the pickle:

> NICK: [Whining to Joe] Kevin is not letting me cut the pickle.
> JOE: Oh, I know! I can pull it away from him and give it back to you. That's an idea!

The boys' conflict, which lasted two and a half times longer than the girls', then proceeded as a struggle between Nick and Joe on the one hand and Kevin on the other.

In comparing the boys' and girls' pickle fights, Sheldon points out that, for the most part, the girls mitigated the conflict and preserved harmony by compromise and evasion. Conflict was more prolonged among the boys, who used more insistence, appeals to rules, and threats of physical violence. However, to say that these little girls and boys used *more* of one strategy or another is not to say that they didn't use the other strategies at all. For example, the boys did attempt compromise, and the girls did attempt physical force. The girls, like the boys, were struggling for control of their play. When Sue says by mistake, *"I'll* give her a whole half," then quickly corrects herself to say, "I'll give her a *whole whole*," she reveals that it is not really the size of the portion that is important to her, but who gets to serve it.

While reading Sheldon's study, I noticed that whereas both Nick and Sue tried to get what they wanted by involving a third child, the alignments they created with the third child, and the dynamics they set in motion, were fundamentally different. Sue appealed to Mary to fulfill someone else's desire; rather than saying that *she* wanted the pickle, she claimed that Lisa wanted it. Nick asserted his own desire for the pickle, she claimed that Lisa wanted it. Nick asserted his own desire for the pickle, and when he couldn't get it on his own, he appealed to Joe to get it for him. Joe then tried to get the pickle by force. In both these scenarios, the children were enacting complex lines of affiliation.

Joe's strong-arm tactics were undertaken not on his own behalf but, chivalrously, on behalf of Nick. By making an appeal in a whining voice, Nick positioned himself as one-down in a hierarchical structure, framing himself as someone in need of protection. When Sue appealed to Mary to relinquish her pickle, she wanted to take the one-up position of serving food. She was fighting not for the right to *have* the pickle, but for the right to *serve* it.... But to accomplish her goal, Sue was depending on Mary's desire to fulfill others' needs.

This study suggests that boys and girls both want to get their way, but they tend to do so differently. Though social norms encourage boys to be openly competitive and girls to be openly cooperative, different situations and activities can result in different ways of behaving. Marjorie Harness Goodwin compared boys and girls engaged in two task-oriented activities: The boys were making slingshots in preparation for a fight, and the girls were making rings. She found that the boys' group was hierarchical: The leader told the others what to do and how to do it. The girls' group was egalitarian: Everyone made suggestions and tended to accept the suggestions of others. But observing the girls in a different activity—playing house—Goodwin found that they too adopted hierarchical structures: The girls who played mothers issued orders to the girls playing children, who in turn sought permission from their play-mothers. Moreover, a girl who was a play-mother was also a kind of manager of the game. This study shows that girls know how to issue orders and operate in a hierarchical structure, but they don't find that mode of behavior appropriate when they engage in task activities with their peers. They do find it appropriate in parent-child relationships, which they enjoy practicing in the form of play.

These worlds of play shed light on the world views of women and men in relationships. The boys' play illuminates why men would be on the lookout for signs they are being put down or told what to do. The chief commodity that is bartered in the boys' hierarchical world is status, and the way to achieve and maintain status is to give orders and get others to follow them. A boy in a low-status position finds himself being pushed around. So boys monitor their relations for subtle shifts in status by keeping track of who's giving orders and who's taking them.

These dynamics are not the ones that drive girls' play. The chief commodity that is bartered in the girls' community is intimacy. Girls monitor their friendships for subtle shifts in alliance, and they seek to be friends with popular girls. Popularity is a kind of status, but it is founded on connection. It also places popular girls in a bind. By doing field work in a junior high school, Donna Eder found that popular girls were paradoxically—and inevitably—disliked. Many girls want to befriend popular girls, but girls' friendships must necessarily be limited, since they entail intimacy rather than large group activities. So a popular girl must reject the overtures of most of the girls who seek her out—with the result that she is branded "stuck up."

The Key Is Understanding

If adults learn their ways of speaking as children growing up in separate social worlds of peers, then conversation between women and men is cross-cultural communication. Although each style is valid on its own terms, misunderstandings arise because the styles are different. Taking a cross-cultural approach to male-female conversations makes it possible to explain why dissatisfactions are justified without accusing anyone of being wrong or crazy.

Learning about style differences won't make them go away, but it can banish mutual mystification and blame. Being able to understand why our partners, friends, and even strangers behave the way they do is a comfort, even if we still don't see things the same way. It makes the world into more familiar territory. And having others understand why we talk and act as we do protects us from the pain of their puzzlement and criticism.

In discussing her novel *The Temple of My Familiar*, Alice Walker explained that a woman in the novel falls in love with a man because she sees in him "a giant ear." Walker went on to remark that although people may think they are falling in love because of sexual attraction or some other force, "really what we're looking for is someone to be able to hear us."

We all want, above all, to be heard—but not merely to be heard. We want to be understood—heard for what we think we are saying, for what we know we meant. With increased understanding of the ways women and men use language should come a decrease in frequency of the complaint, "You just don't understand."

Chemical Reaction

~

BY

BONNIE

BISHOP

i gave my daughter a perm
last night she'd been begging for one
for years o how i love you she squealed
when i brought home the ingredients
her eyes were shut tight
while i applied the potion

this morning after fluffing it
up she left for the skating rink
without her skates
now i know my reason
for waiting so long

Young, Gay—and Alone

BY

BARRY CAME

O n his young life, Jonathan Horsford's sexuality has driven him to the brink of suicide on more than one occasion. He was 16 the first time it happened, newly arrived in Toronto after a childhood spent in Nova Scotia. While walking along a downtown street, he encountered an adult—and obviously gay—man approaching from the opposite direction. "The guy looked right into my eyes as we passed," Horsford remembers, "and at that moment I knew that I, too, was gay." Horsford, now 20, and a third-year science student at Montreal's McGill University, vividly recalls being overwhelmed at the time by a sense of shame. "I felt naked," he says. "I thought everyone in that big sophisticated city, unlike the folks back home, could see me for what I really was. I wanted to run away and hide." In despair, he retreated to his parents' house, locked himself in his room and swallowed "a whole bunch of aspirins."

Jonathan Horsford survived the incident. But many youngsters facing the same, or similar, situations do not. They are, as Horsford was, teenagers utterly bewildered by the direction in which their emerging sexuality is heading. Some quickly realize that they are gay or lesbian. A few view themselves as mysteriously diseased. Others are merely confused, haunted by an attraction to members of the same sex that is looked upon with undisguised contempt by their own peers and by society at large. And whatever the state of their sexual development, most lead troubled interior lives. "These kids carry a terrible added weight at a really critical time," says Montreal social worker William Ryan.

The burden can often wreak havoc. Every year in the United

States, 5000 young people between the ages of 15 and 24 take their own lives. And according to the U.S. Department of Health and Human Services, fully 30 per cent of those suicides are directly related to the emotional turmoil over sexual orientation. Suicide aside, U.S. research also suggests that the same turmoil leads to high school dropout rates, higher levels of drug and alcohol abuse, parental rejection, homelessness and prostitution. While there are no comparable Canadian studies, there is little reason to believe that the situation is much different in this country. But outside of a few isolated programs located almost entirely in major urban centres, there are few places where a sexually troubled youngster can seek out guidance and support.

The result is isolation, of a particularly trying variety. "It's the worst kind of loneliness," says Jason, a 20-year-old McGill history major, who asked that his identity be masked. Jason has yet to inform his parents in the southern Ontario town where he was born and raised that he has finally "come out" and entered a long-term relationship with another male student. "I realized I was different from a very early age, but I could never admit it, not even to myself for a long time," he says. "The images were just too negative. There were times in high school when I wondered if I was the only one on the face of the planet. And yet there was no one I could turn to—not my parents, certainly not my friends. When you're a teenager, it's the last thing you want your friends to know."

Many teenage gays, faced with the prospect of rejection—or worse—from friends and relatives, resort to leading double lives. Andrew Moulden, 19, attended Westdale Secondary School in Hamilton, Ont. Although he claims to have been aware of his homosexuality his "whole life," he attempted to portray the opposite image: at age 16, he had been dating the same girl for two years. "It can get really confusing," he says. "You go out with your friends to a bar and you go out with women, but you know all the time that it's an act—it's no good for you." Moulden, now studying social sciences at McMaster University, tired of playing the role and openly declared his homosexuality when he was 16. But it was not easy. "The hardest thing is fear of the unknown," he says, "fear of losing your friends, fear of how your family is going to react."

Fear appears to be a constant factor in the lives of almost all young people who think—or accept the fact—that they are gay. If they openly confess their sexual orientation or doubts, they face verbal and perhaps even physical harassment. If they keep quiet, they remain lonely and alienated. "It's always there," says Robbie, a 23-year-old Montreal lesbian. "In high school, I was so afraid of my own sexuality that I grew aggressively more homophobic the closer I got to coming out. If anyone even so much as hinted I might be lesbian, I would lash out in anger." Despite the distress, however, few young gays or lesbians feel that they have any choice in the matter.

The Perilous Balancing Act of Growing Up Male

BY

ANGELA
PHILLIPS

The killing of James Bulger by two boys aged just 10 at the time has focused attention on why boys often turn to violence, yet girls rarely do so.

Lone motherhood, economic deprivation, bad housing: We can argue from all sides about the relative effects of these three factors on the behavior and development of young people. Yet no matter which way you cut the statistics, the factor that is always closely correlated with criminality is the Y-chromosome.

Generally speaking, men are responsible for 90 per cent of indictable offences. Sixty young men are incarcerated for every one young woman. Why does nobody ever ask why it is that so few young women, living in exactly the same unemployment, the same bad housing and cared for by the same lone mother as their male peers, end up in prison?

Let us reflect a moment on what girls are raised to become. For a girl, the future is not far away. She is brought up by women, surrounded by women, women care for her, and she watches them about their daily work: it is women (not necessarily their mothers) who clean, cook and care for her and her siblings. She may also see women leaving for some other work but it is the work that she can watch and learn herself that she will copy in her play.

Little girls know by the age of 3 that they will grow up to become mothers, to run a home and, if their mothers have jobs they may include that too. From an adult point of view, this obsession with homemaking may seem rather limited but from the point of view of a 3-year-old, the role of mother is a rich one full of material to practise on. A girl can be a mother, plus something else.

For a male toddler, that early picture is very different. Few men are closely involved with him, he rarely sees a real man do anything he can relate to. He doesn't see his father working, talking to his friends, cleaning the floor. He watches, when he can, and learns as much as he is able, but a male child learns most of the early lessons in masculinity from snatches and pictures and glimpses of the male world. His father may swoop down and throw him in the air but he isn't there to show him how a man does whatever men do.

And I am not talking only about the boys of single mothers. I doubt that the sons of male cabinet ministers see more of their fathers than the sons of many divorced parents.

You have only to spend a short time in a day-care to see that by the age of 3, most little girls are already behaving like women: they are simply practising being grown up.

Most little boys have no idea what it is they are supposed to be (I say most, not all, for some boys have just the same level of inner certainty as a girl, only not so many of them). So they try out

being like mummy and the girls tell them that boys can't behave like that. They try crying and asking to go home and they are told that boys can't behave like that.

But what *is* a boy supposed to grow up to be? Batman? Bart Simpson? Where does a father go when he closes the door in the morning? Perhaps the reason why so many boys run around and shout a lot is because they don't know what else to do. They don't have a complex role to inhabit, or a joint understanding of an imaginary world in which to play together. The only thing they know about what it is to be male is that it *isn't* like being a girl.

They start to define their whole sense of themselves, not in a positive sense as "like" someone but in a negative sense, as unlike the people who surround them: the mothers, teachers, child care workers and all those competent and organized little girls.

Soon one of the worst taunts a male child can use to his peers is to call him "a girl." However, nobody can survive with a vacuum in the place where they are supposed to keep their identity. Boys *have* to learn how to be boys. They have to find out what it is that they should be which is

not just different from girls but uniquely masculine.

In the absence of close multi-dimensional male figures to learn from that information must come from their peers. By the time they are 7, the coercive process of masculinization is well under way. Boys mercilessly tease those who do not conform to the group idea of masculinity.

Some will take these ideas home and be able to check them and shape them against the real life figures of their fathers or grandfathers. If the shapes fit, they will move on more confidently. So, a boy who play-fights at school and comes home to a father who wrestles with him in the garden will feel an inner sense of confidence that he is doing something that men do—and he will do more of it.

Perhaps this is why, in various studies quoted in *The Role of Fathers in Child Development,* edited by Michael Lamb, boys who have no father, or whose fathers left before they turned 5, are rated less aggressive than other boys.

Of course, there are many fathers who teach their sons that fighting is bad. The boy then has to work out who is right: the boys at school or his Dad. Who is the *real* man?

A lot will depend on how he feels about his father. A child who feels happy with the person he is at home, and secure in the love of his parents, may simply adapt to the requirements of school by having a school persona and a gentler home persona. He will have learned that masculinity is not one-dimensional. So who are the boys who are likely to end up getting into trouble?

The most vulnerable are those who have difficulty with their school work; those whose parents teach them to be troublemakers by their own example; those whose parents are unable or unwilling to spend time with their children or who abuse them and those who have experienced family conflict. Girls are also likely to be adversely affected but they are far less likely to demonstrate their unease by getting into trouble with the law.

In the years between 5 and 10, boys desperately need to enforce a common understanding of male behavior, a collective male identity to shore up from the outside the lack of a confident masculinity on the inside.

To consort with a child whose behavior doesn't fit the accepted standard is to risk being out of step with this collectively engineered picture of masculine behavior. Those who don't fit will be edged out in order to create a clearer idea of what it is to be a proper boy.

By secondary school age, a significant minority of these boys have not regained confidence or been allowed "back in" by their peers. These are the ones who will be prepared to do just about anything to be accepted as one of the boys. So it is little wonder that they are more likely than more confident peers to be those who are unable to say no to trouble and to get sucked in to attention-seeking behavior which screams "I *am* a boy, notice me!"

Toughening up is a characteristic experience of boys across society from the top private schools to the schools in poor neighborhoods. Though there are certainly some boys who manage to negotiate the school system by using charm and wit to stay out of trouble, few go through the experience without an awareness of the violence which lurks just a glance away.

To an uncertain 12-year-old, the streets are filled with menace. One of the early lessons a boy needs to learn is just how to walk the street without, ever, looking an older boy in the eye, because to make eye contact is to invite conflict.

Those at the top of the tree will use this acquired toughness to succeed in business. Those at the bottom are more likely to use the same toughness to succeed on the street. Parents bringing up children in an environment in which crime is the only apparent way out of poverty will have a hard time keeping their sons safe from the bad influence of boys their own age.

Industrial and economic change and the changing role of women have had a devastating effect on male morale. There are adjustments to be made, but to make those changes our boys need to have men around them who are not cardboard cut-out figures like Superman.

Nor do they need those strong silent men who leave the house every morning and shut the door on their families. They need fathers who will teach their sons that family life is something that they can take part in on equal terms with women.

It will take a long time to produce a generation of fathers like that. In the meantime, something has to be done to provide today's boys with a new image of masculinity to capture their imagination at the crucial point when they realize that they are not going to grow up to be like Mum.

The Fitness Industry's Empty Promise

~

BY

JODY

BENJAMIN

ur society has a big fat problem and the fitness industry is only making it worse.

As a fitness instructor, I feel a strange mixture of pride and shame. I'm proud of the women who come to my class and feel a sense of support and community there. I'm proud of giving them a positive and creative way of experiencing themselves as physical beings.

Yet, when I tell people I'm a fitness instructor I feel like I'm saying I wear polyester and sell used cars—I'm slimy. I usually add some inane disclaimer. "My classes are different," or "I really hate the fitness industry," or "I don't pinch people's fat and tell them they're seven pounds overweight."

I stopped taking workshops for fitness leaders years ago as my awareness of women's body-image issues grew and after a few particularly shocking experiences. The last workshop I attended was on eating disorders. When I read about it I thought: "Hooray! Someone's finally acknowledging this as an important issue that leaders need to be very informed about because of their position of influence."

Fat chance. In reality it was some psychiatrist drumming up business for his practice. The first thing he did was pass around a photo of himself when he was 200 pounds heavier.

Tacky! He talked a bit about compulsive eating and how dieting leads to more compulsive eating patterns—useful information—but he was basically saying: Here's my phone number. Send all your fat ladies to me and I'll fix them. After a few questions like, "What's the best way to lose five pounds by Christmas?"

we tied pillows around our bellies and someone led us through a basic workout called "the fat burner."

The argument about the heart-rate chart was the last straw for me. These were certified fitness instructors and some were reading the chart incorrectly. That's the first thing a fitness instructor should know. I found the whole thing an insult to my intelligence and disturbing evidence of the lack of awareness and concern in the fitness leadership of the time.

That was 1986. I never went back. I've been underground and simmering ever since. I haven't stopped teaching. I love it. It's essential to my well-being and I have a strong commitment to the women who tell me how important it is to their well-being.

But teaching fitness is a stupid career. You can't teach eight hours a day, five days a week. You are only paid on a per class basis. There's no prep-time payment and no help to pay for supplies or courses. It's the teachers who typically have to keep themselves in lycra and lipstick, Reeboks and records.

Have you priced a good pair of running shoes lately? Sports bras are right up there, too. For a fashion plate who likes leopard-skin lycra, I could easily see losing money at this job. And yet the fitness industry is a multi-million-dollar monster that's making big bucks for somebody.

Our society is getting sucked in by empty promises of health and beauty. Physical fitness used to be a natural byproduct of a life of hard work, like farming or fun, like social dancing. Now fitness has become a pseudo-science which, by nature, sets standards and generalizes about what is normal and acceptable. We also live in a society that is paranoid and prejudiced about fat.

That combination spells disaster for a naturally heavy person who heads toward their neighborhood fitness facility or weight loss clinic. I say naturally heavy because there are studies that show that everyone has a genetic predisposition to a certain weight and the body will fight to maintain that weight.

So, in most cases, the more you diet, the fatter you get. To maintain one's natural weight requires a lifestyle of variety, moderation and common sense. Drastic diets for quick results get quick disappointments.

Exercise is the same. If it's moderate exercise that's enjoyable, regular and done out of caring for oneself, it is essential to good health. Sporadic intense exercise done out of guilt and self-hatred is detrimental and even dangerous to one's health. With class sizes that range from 50 to 150, I can see how many fitness instructors are failing to communicate these important points to their participants.

How is someone who has never exercised before, going to know what it feels like to exercise, especially when surrounded by 149 other people who look like 21-year-old experts, and they are led by a teacher on a platform yelling into a microphone above the thumping dance mix? No wonder statistics for injuries in aerobics classes are so startling.

Another essential ingredient is physical awareness and ease. I like to leave a lot of room for interpretation in my classes. I teach the steps and then invite people to change them to suit themselves; according to their energy level, to accommodate an injury or just for creative expression.

I want people in my class to play and experiment with their bodies; to discover what does and does not feel right for them, and to respect the wisdom of their bodies.

People, especially women, need to be encouraged to look to themselves for advice. The "expert" is not always the best one to run to for answers. For example, fitness testing is gratuitous and usually detrimental to the user. I can name several women, including myself, who have been told they were up to 10 pounds overweight after scoring well on all the important parts of the test such as cardiovascular fitness and muscle endurance.

Advice like that can set off a bulge battle that lasts a lifetime with very serious repercussions. It encourages women, who were content, to scrutinize every pound. For others, it could be the catalyst that triggers compulsive/obsessive behavior patterns. It is shocking, but not surprising, that up to 80 per cent of women have some degree of eating disorder.

Until we can learn to celebrate our bodies, whatever size or shape they are, and to care for our bodies in loving ways, we will continue to foster a society full of bodies misshapen by starvation or stuffed by compulsion. Let's start by allowing people to find their natural selves by accepting them as they are. It should not be assumed that any woman over a size 10 wants or needs to lose weight; she has the right to feel comfortable and respected anywhere she goes.

Studies Find Body Builders Suffer 'Reverse Anorexia'

BY

SHELLEY PAGE

A disturbing condition being called "reverse anorexia" or the obsessive "drive to bulk up" has been found among male body builders in two ground-breaking studies.

Researchers at the Ottawa Civic Hospital eating-disorders clinic and at Harvard University are alarmed after discovering severe body-image dissatisfaction and distortion among some men in the weight rooms and gyms across North America. In some cases, these big, muscular men look in the mirror and see themselves as 90-pound weaklings. The researchers have linked these attitudes to obsessive weightlifting, taking steroids, and binging and purging.

"I found men who were large and muscular, but they would not go to the beach, not take their shirts off in a swimming pool, they'd wear baggy sweat clothes to avoid being seen as small," says Dr. Harrison Pope, a psychiatrist at Harvard who has just completed a study of the attitudes and habits of 156 body builders in Boston and Los Angeles.

Using the term "reverse anorexia," Pope says many of the men in his study exhibit the opposite symptoms of anorexic women who starve themselves until they're extremely thin, but still see themselves as heavy. These women often wear baggy clothes to hide their perceived chubbiness.

Dr. Arthur Blouin, head of psychology at the Civic, found evidence of image dissatisfaction in body builders after studying the practices across Ontario of 140 men involved in body building, Taekwondo and running.

"We're interested in whether or not there is evolving a body-image type of disorder in men, similar to what we see in women," Blouin says. Blouin does not like the term, "reverse anorexia" and instead calls the obsessive weight-lifting and steroid-taking the "drive to bulk up." "Anorexia (in women) is a multifaceted, complicated thing. It's not like a sock you can just turn inside out."

Both researchers stressed that not all body builders have these image problems. And the researchers are not sure whether men develop the body-image disorders first, and then head to the gym to pump up their self-esteem. Pope says these men might develop the image disorder after getting into a gym with other huge, intimidating men.

Pope "stumbled" on to the problems while researching the psychological effects of steroid use. Among the 156 body builders, 88 were past or present steroid users, while 68 were not. Pope says he found 16 cases of what he terms "reverse anorexia," all of which occurred in the group of steroid users.

Pope says some of these men with "reverse anorexia" started using steroids as a way to combat their feelings of small-ness. But he thinks others developed "reverse anorexia" after they started taking steroids. "Their preoccupation became more severe."

Surprisingly, four of this group had anorexia nervosa when they were younger. "The probability of looking at 156 American men and stumbling on four who'd had anorexia would be less than one in a million," Pope says.

Blouin studied men involved in Taekwondo, running, and body building because they were individual sports and because each has an element of defence. "You know the old image of the skinny guy on the beach who gets sand kicked in his face," he says.

A man gets bigger and stronger lifting weights, and can defend himself with a martial art such as Taekwondo. As for running, "I guess they can always run away."

Blouin and Carleton University student Gary Goldfield surveyed both competitive and recreational participants across Ontario. They modified surveys normally used to assess image problems among sufferers of anorexia and bulimia.

Blouin says they found only one steroid user among the runners, no steroid use among the martial artists, but 75 per cent steroid use among the body builders. He found no image problems among the runners or martial artists.

Some body builders, many of whom are already 20 to 30 per cent larger than the average guy because of bulking up, see themselves as five per cent underweight, Blouin says. He would not say how many because he was looking for patterns. He says there are extremes of attitudes and it's difficult to illustrate using numbers.

He says this type of intense dissatisfaction appears to lead to self-destructive behavior such as steroid use, and in some cases, the same binging and purging seen in female bulimics.

The body builders tended to use diuretics instead of vomiting to rid themselves of food after a binge. Blouin points out that researchers were often puzzled why some women with body-image problems exhibited self-destructive behavior such as starvation and vomiting, while men didn't. It has been hypo-thesized that with the advent of more male fashion magazines and more pressure to look good, more men would develop eating disorders such as anorexia nervosa or bulimia. That didn't happen.

This research shows that men do exhibit self-destructive behavior, just not the same kind. "There is a notion amongst both anorexics and bulimics and these men that their value as a person is linked to the body. The size of your hips or biceps," says Blouin. "But for both groups it doesn't work. It doesn't improve your self-esteem."

Both researchers say they'd like to do more research to see if education programs can be developed for young men.

Thin Equals Happy? Fat Chance

~

BY

TESS

FRAGOULIS

I am a harrassed woman. Not by an insensitive male-power boss, or by irate male co-workers railing against the promotion of women, but by other women. And not just recently. This has been a lifelong affliction. I am ready to break my silence.

As a child I was considered underweight by the medical establishment. One cold-hearted female physician gave my mother an ultimatum. I was to gain 10 pounds within a month—or else. I gagged at the thought of stuffing all that excess food down my throat. Luckily, my mother had the sense not to listen. After all, I was a happy, healthy child who ate when I was hungry; a habit that has not left me.

My grandmother, on the other hand, a rotund Greek traditionalist, did not agree. Her favourite expression was, "Eat it or wear it." I always pictured myself with an overturned bowl of noodles on my head, sauce spilling into my ears, and I wondered if she would really do it.

She would make me sit at the kitchen table for hours, and I mastered rolling one bite of food around in my mouth long enough that even she gave up on my ever finishing the meal. She also made me eat fatty meat, which disgusted me, because it would supposedly put meat on my bones. "Skin and bones," she would pronounce distastefully, shake her head and frown as if it were her failure. I felt guilty and scared, as if I had some disease that was not only fatal but was an embarrassment and a disappointment to my family. I was a bad apple. I hung my head in shame.

In elementary school they called me Toothpick. In high school I graduated to Chicken Legs and Flat-as-a-board, because my body just stretched out; gangly arms, arrow-sharp legs and no filler. The chiding subsided to a certain degree when my hormones kicked in by the age of 14 and drew in the curves. Unfortunately, the running commentary did not demise.

Recently, at a feminist lecture on body image and the billion-dollar weight-loss industry, the speaker stated that nature did not make women with long legs, slim hips and ample bosoms. A few women turned around in their seats and eyed me suspiciously. Was I real, or just a hapless victim of the media campaign to torture women through diet and plastic surgery? Obviously, I couldn't be a natural woman, their looks told me. And if I were, what business did I have at their event anyway?

I have been blatantly asked if I'm anorexic, if I've ever been overweight, if I'm really going to eat that cheese croissant. Dieting women feel no restraint against barraging me with their insecurities, lamenting about how they looked just like me when they were younger, how they could look just like me if only they exercised more, gave up potato chips, were born with a different gene pool. They go on about how lucky I am, and never think to ask whether I have any problems. Even when I had cysts sprouting out of my face, all they could see was my weight compared with theirs.

One woman I met at a party insinuated that I must never have romantic problems because I'm thin. Well guess again, girls. My weight does not make me immune to standups, breakups and general disappointment. Ironically, I would need a thicker skin to avoid the inevitable war wounds in the battle of the sexes.

The saddest thing is that all these women were beautiful, whatever shape, whatever size, and they couldn't see it. Instead, they resented me and shut me out.

Some may say I speak from a privileged position, and that I don't know what it's like to live on the wrong end of a society that idolizes air-brushed images of wispy women. I beg to differ. There is no privilege in being accepted because of my looks instead of my ideas, my wit or my abilities. It's demeaning. And there is no comfort in being constantly sized up by both men and women, instantly judged as happy, desirable, sick or a threat, as if there is no substance beneath the skin and bones. I'd rather be admired for who I am and for what I have accomplished.

My message to women obsessed with their weight is that in the grand scheme of things, a few pounds more or less are not going to change your life, except where there are health concerns. You will not be more advantaged, admired, loved or accepted. My trials and tribulations are the same as yours, those inherent in being a woman, such as getting equal pay for equal work.

My entire life, I have been made to feel as self-conscious about my thin body as I imagine overweight women feel. Actually, I sometimes think that a few extra pounds might give me more clout, more "weight," but that too is a symptom. All women are affected, directly or indirectly, by a society that objectifies them and dictates body image. There is no hierarchy, there are no constants, there is no ideal weight, and there is no way to win. Must we make each other feel inadequate too?

The Selling of Addiction to Women

~

BY

CAROL MOOG

everly is an art director. She works with images all the time, and knows just how advertising tries to work on her. And she's fought hard to maintain her independence—to be herself. But I hear her talk about her friends, and she always ends up comparing *them* to some famous face: "Oh, you know her, she looks like Cheryl Tiegs." And when I ask her whom *she* looks like, Beverly glances down and shrugs, "Oh, nobody, just plain old me."

Everybody struggles to develop a sense of security, a sense of personal identity, but most of us end up constantly glancing around us—and that includes supercharged media models. We hate ourselves for it, especially if we can see exactly what buttons the advertisers are pushing, but many of us buy into the images just enough to wish we could do it all...be that thin or that rich or that happy or that confident. And then, telling ourselves that we're not affected by advertising, we find ourselves shelling out for the product.

It's one thing for a woman to purchase too many cosmetics or jeans in a convoluted effort to gain love and acceptance by measuring up to Madison Avenue. At that point she's buying into the cultural myth brought to us through the wonders of advertising, that women must be young, ingenuous, gorgeous, and innocuous. But what about when she's being lured with products which are dangerous, even lethal, and addictive? The stakes are much higher, and the trade-off for a woman isn't just a genuine sense of self, it may be her life.

Young women comprise America's fastest-growing population of smokers and their rate of lung cancer has increased fivefold in the past two decades, finally beating breast cancer in the mortality sweepstakes. When the tobacco industry went fishing for women back in the late 1920s, what baited its advertisers' hooks? Promises of slender sophistication, pleasure, and freedom. When the tobacco industry hunts women of the 1990s what are its magic bullets? Promises of slender sophistication, pleasure and freedom.

When Lucky Strike developed its famous slogan, "Reach for a Lucky Instead of a Sweet," complete with an image of a young, slim woman emerging from the shadow of an older, fatter self, Lucky sales skyrocketed 215 per cent. The marketing success of Virginia Slims, powered by images of svelte, fashionable models liberated from sepia scenes of woman's drudgery and shapelessness before the Tobacco Liberation, is similarly impressive.

How can the same advertising strategies continue to be so effective with women? To be a smoker in America is to distinctly lose points in the winning-friends-and-influencing people department. Everywhere smokers turn, they are faced with stomach-churning medical counsel, dramatic spasms of hacking,

disdainful glowerings and unsolicited advice on quitting. When I'm with a smoker who answers "Smoking, please," to the hostess' seating question, the scene always reminds me of the one in Monty Python's *Life of Brian*, where, on Good Friday, prisoners are directed toward the proper sentencing: "Crucifixion, right this way." Why are so many women choosing to hang themselves on tobacco's cross?

Despite the real societal changes that have occurred in the culture with regard to women's career and role opportunities, little genuine progress has occurred psychologically. Repeatedly in my clinical practice, repeatedly in consumer interviews, I hear the stories of women who, underneath their mantles of intellect and achievement, remain addicted to external approval. They may look all grown-up on the outside, but inside many still have the insatiable needs and insecurities of children who have never been accepted and loved as competent, separate individuals.

Drugs such as tobacco and, of course, alcohol, offer transient solutions to the problems of self-esteem and identity, not only because of the stress-reducing properties of these substances themselves, but because of the heightened independence and self-fulfillment that advertising constantly associates with their use. The particular images that tobacco and alcohol advertisers rely on most are those that feed into women's underlying sense of themselves as emotionally empty and vulnerable. They offer up tantalizing glimpses of endless pleasure and vitality.

In an ad for Newport Lights, we see a young woman deliriously happy to be encased in a bizarre two-person sweater, seemingly designed to demonstrate the joy of symbiosis, for the purpose of selling the fantasy that she'll be "Alive with Pleasure!" She has no identity as a separate individual, her very life drawn from her connection with her masculine counterpart. As long as she smokes Newport Lights, her needs for emotional bonding will be met. Never mind that we see her hands outstretched beyond what she's already got, seeking still more "pleasure." She is addicted and insatiable—just the kind of woman a cigarette company wants her to stay.

Decoding the Real Message
R. J. Reynold's ad for More cigarettes taps into these feelings even more explicitly. Its appeal depends upon the fantasy of filling the bottomless pit of need and longing that drives the insecurities of so many women. Regressive desires for on-demand feedings are embodied by the cigarette brand name itself—*More*. Ask for it by name and you verbally reinforce both the addiction and the psychological drive behind it.

The model shown is close to a paragon of the cultural definition of feminine sophistication. She radiates self-confidence and insouciance (who cares if her elegant white dress gets dirtier by the pier?). This image of ease and individuality acts as a decoy to the unconscious question: How could this woman possibly be in a state of constant need? She seems to have it all: to want "more," and, as the subhead instructs, to "never settle for less," must be hallmarks of a mature, desirable individual.

But this ad goes the extra mile in getting its target to identify with this image: the green water and pier, the huge "More" across the top of the page, and the double white strip to its right, all precisely match the design of the cigarette package she holds. She *is* the package. When you inhale a More cigarette, you internalize her image. And what is this role model's "favourite indulgence," as the body copy asks? Her "special reward" isn't really smoking (after all, smoking is a dirty habit which leads to unsightly spots on the lungs and she's all in white), it's "the time I spend with More." This denial of the addiction, the seeming innocence of this simple pleasure, is given heavy advertising support. And what is by her side to further uncouple her ties to the reality of her lethal "indulgence?" A glass of wine.

For addictions to maintain their hold, a huge amount of psychic energy must be invested in the defensive denial of the consequences of the behaviour. Newport Stripes offers a stunning example of this kind of psychological sleight-of-hand in an ad which has as its centerpiece two hysterically laughing, nearly identical blonde women cuddling big, fat, jolly snow "babies" on their laps. They're little-girl-women-mommies, in exuberant good health (a glow heightened by the intensely hot pink colour of the surrounding page). Their cigarettes are "smooth and delicate" (like a baby's skin) and they are "light, refreshing" (and harmless) as the candy features on their "babies." Why do so many young women smoke? For one thing, their mothers do. The messages in this ad insidiously support continuing the habit in the next generation by showing these delightful young mothers who enjoy "the latest in pleasure" and have fine chubby children (to whom they will pass on their addictions). The Surgeon General's Warning is the *pièce de résistance* in this ad's denial of reality, and ironically, the selection of warnings is purely by chance: "Smoking by Pregnant Women May Result in Fetal Injury, Premature Birth, and Low Birth Weight."

Women are constantly portrayed in tobacco and alcohol advertising as creatures of pleasure who, because of their childlike freedom from the ordinary humdrum of reality (growing old, getting cancer, becoming an alcoholic) live lives of fun, fulfillment and romance. Lack of an adult sense of identity and accountability is transmuted, through the wizardry of advertising's fog and mirrors into the imagery of women with independent spirits. The illusions of freedom obscure their slavery to their addictions.

There they are, jogging along a perfect beach foamed with surf, two beautifully constructed women talking about a man (what else *do* women talk about?) whom they both seem to admire very much. They are interchangeable, and the headline could be coming from either: "He loves my mind. *And* he drinks Johnnie Walker."

How unfettered. The model's insecurity about being loved for *who* she is ("my mind") is so profound that she and her friend display their bikinied backsides, just to be sure. They are mirror images of each other and need each other's smiling agreement to shore up the illusion that it is natural and somehow intelligent for a woman to equate a man's valuing her "mind" with her appreciation of his brand of whiskey.

Regardless of the modern cultural wellspring of support and admiration for intellectually accomplished women, advertising reflects and magnifies women's insecurity about whether their acumen will really result in a man's approval. This piece for Johnnie Walker takes no chances and shows women who have enough sense to know that they have minds, but keep them tucked under cute little baseball caps while they show their least threatening assets to the guys. As the tag line says, "Good taste is always an asset."

People who are secure enough to develop an enduring, mutual, affectionate relationship with another person have accomplished an extraordinarily difficult psychological task. Too often both men and women get stuck in a desperate determination not to expose their insecurities as they frantically try to fill a sense of emptiness with packaged facsimiles of love. This culture holds up an endless array of tempting surrogates to emotion, packaged like passion and romance but containing alcohol as their main ingredients.

Women searching for intimacy through fantasy are particularly vulnerable to this approach. And Gilbey's gin reels them in with the glamour of black and white film star lovers, filling the page with the sultry glow of moonlight and caresses while the headline works its magic, and begins to construct a script about the forging of relationships built completely on fantasy and held together by shared alcoholism: "The men never asked, the women never told, and martinis were their passion." Translation: "Shut up and drink, dear."

The copy promotes the endless pursuit of passion ("When one look could ignite your heart like a million candles") in lieu of a mature, enduring relationship. The pursuit of passion is fueled by a sense of inner deadness, and as such, is doomed to failure—even if it succeeds. The cycle is truly vicious: the inevitable loss of passion leaves an ever-increasing sense of worthlessness and insecurity. In other words, it's a winner if an advertiser wants to hook women on alcohol. As the copy tells us, after World War I, people were "drinking in hopes they would make up for what was lost." Drink to try to feel something, to try to feel real. Gilbey's tells its target consumers that martinis, which should, of course, be made with its brand of gin, "Weren't meant just for sipping." Yes, it takes a lot of booze to mask the pain and, as the story ends, bring back "the taste for passion." And what does Gilbey's, this dealer of delusions, call itself? The Authentic Gin.

The more women try to fill themselves up by propping up the *outside*, the more terrified they are about exposing who they really are on the *inside*. The discrepancy becomes too great, and the investment in the decoy self becomes too high to risk losing whatever security it does provide. Probably the single biggest barrier to love is the fear of psychological exposure, of being found out and found lacking. The shame can be stupefying. The denial of reality can become all-consuming. When advertisers of products like tobacco and alcohol lock in with people's deepest fears of being unlovable, they offer their products and images as the roads to love, when what they really provide are tickets to addiction.

Sonnet 130

BY

WILLIAM

SHAKESPEARE

My mistress' eyes are nothing like the sun;
Coral is far more red than her lips' red;
If snow be white, why then her breasts are dun;
If hairs be wires, black wires grow on her head.
I have seen roses damasked, red and white,
But no such roses see I in her cheeks;
And in some perfumes is there more delight
Than in the breath that from my mistress reeks.
I love to hear her speak, yet well I know
That music hath a far more pleasing sound;
I grant I never saw a goddess go;
My mistress, when she walks, treads on the ground.
And yet, by heaven, I think my love as rare
As any she belied with false compare.

The Garden of Love

BY

WILLIAM

BLAKE

I went to the Garden of Love,
And saw what I never had seen:
A Chapel was built in the midst,
Where I used to play on the green.

And the gates of this Chapel were shut,
And "Thou shalt not" writ over the door;
So I turn'd to the Garden of Love
That so many sweet flowers bore;

And I saw it was filled with graves,
And tomb-stones where flowers should be;
And Priests in black gowns were walking their rounds,
And binding with briars my joys & desires.

The
Poet's
Visit

~

BY

NAHID

RACHLIN

Mina and Simin saw each other almost every day after school even though they lived on opposite sides of the city. They had been friends since elementary school and now they were in the tenth grade. They remained close friends in spite of the difference in their temperaments. Simin was quiet and poetic, Mina outspoken. Although Simin was less intense than Mina in expressing her dissatisfaction with their lives, their larger view of things coincided. They agreed they would have to fight hard not to become typical wives and mothers, not to marry men selected for them by their families. One way to avoid this was to refuse to marry at all or, better, to convince their parents to send them out of the country to study.

"I want so much to go away," Mina told Simin over and over like a chant.

"Yes, somewhere far away," Simin said.

"Everything is so gray here, even the uniforms we have to wear to school," Mina said, keenly aware of how dusty the streets were, how withered the trees, of idle men sitting in doorways, of the many women wrapped in dark *chadors.*

They went to foreign movies, read novels, escaping into the worlds created by them.

Their families were very different from each other. Simin's father was a colonel, a rather reclusive man. She had one brother who was quiet and studious. Her mother was a lively woman who hummed to herself when not talking. Her parents, as well as her grandmother and her bachelor uncle, who visited often, doted on her, paying close attention to her daily activities—how many hours of sleep she got, how much and what she ate at each meal, how much time she spent studying. Sometimes her grandmother would hunch over her on the floor and comb Simin's long hair as if she were still a child.

Mina's father was a lawyer, her mother a drained-looking woman who spent all her energy running a household of six children. Mina's sisters and brothers, some older than she, some younger, all seemed to suffer from insoluble problems. The oldest sister, for instance, a pretty, romantic girl, was in love with one of her high school teachers but about to be married off to the rich son of a merchant. She sighed a lot and hardly talked to anyone. Another one of Mina's sisters, a year younger, refused to go to school. She spent her time knitting, or was just content to follow her mother around. The two live-in servants always quarreled.

"You're lucky to be so close to your family," Mina said to Simin.

"I guess so," Simin said in her mild, affectionate way. "But you have other things. Everyone notices you. Look at the way boys stare at you on the street."

Mina had very smooth olive skin, black hair and black eyes, and a mole on her upper lip. Her figure was round and voluptuous. Simin was thin, pale, with chestnut hair and light hazel eyes.

"But I don't like any of them," Mina said.

They were temporarily diverted from their usual concerns when Mina learned that Mahmood Ardavani, a distinguished writer-poet, would be visiting Teheran on business and that her father would be advising him on legal matters. In fact Ardavani would stay at their house for one or two nights—he and Mina's father had a mutual friend from their university years.

The news totally stirred Mina and Simin. They were both avid readers of Ardavani's writing, mainly his prose, which appeared regularly in the *Teheran Monthly* and sometimes in the equally distinguished magazine, *Setareh*. He was a popular, rather slick writer.

Simin and Mina liked his work mostly for its foreign settings and its subject matter—male-female relationships. Once one of his novels, serialized in *Setareh,* abruptly terminated with an editorial note: "Withdrawn by the author for personal reasons." It had been very disappointing to them to stop reading the novel as it was approaching its climax. It also had doubly aroused their curiosity about Ardavani. They wondered why he had withdrawn the story and whether it had been autobiographical. It was about an Iranian girl, studying in the United States, who fell in love with an Iranian writer visiting the campus. He ignored her for the attentions of an older American woman.

"I can't believe he's actually going to be staying at your house," Simin said.

"You'll be coming over, of course, and you'll probably see as much of him as I will."

He would be arriving in two weeks. Mina and Simin began to plan. They took out his books from the library and read them. They even had dresses made for the occasion. It was late spring and they chose printed cotton fabric, one with bright butterflies, the other with tiny squares and circles. Simin picked the one with the butterflies. The tailor promised to have them ready within a week.

The day before Mahmood Ardavani was expected they picked up their dresses from the tailor, then they went to the little garden restaurant around the corner from the tailor to have ice cream. They sat in the shade of a huge sycamore tree and each had a dish of ice cream full of hard pieces of vanilla. Several familiar figures came in—the boy who always wore a yellow shirt and a black tie and hung around outside their high school, and another boy, tall and gaunt with startling gray eyes who also frequently walked up and down in front of their school. These boys had sometimes followed them, from one winding street to another, becoming invisible at a curve but soon appearing again. Now they came and sat at tables not far from theirs and began to look at them intently.

Mina and Simin automatically turned their backs on them and began to whisper about Mahmood Ardavani.

"I don't know what I'm going to say to him," Simin said.

"I can't imagine being face to face with him. He's so handsome too." In his pictures he looked middle-aged, with penetrating black eyes, and curly brown hair growing rather wildly around his head. It made Mina think of a young man she had once furtively kissed at a wedding.

Finally they left the restaurant and each went their separate ways. At home Mina noticed that her mother was already preparing for Ardavani's arrival too, getting a room ready for him to sleep in, planning menus for breakfast and dinner. Their house was large and outlandish, located in the noisy center of Ghanat Abad Avenue. It had many rooms with doors that rattled in the wind and no longer closed completely. In the summer the cement that covered the ground around the house burned like fire and in the winter it became ice cold. Mina's mother complained about the house even more than usual now. "I have a lawyer husband, we deserve better than this." She walked around the house with one of the servants, dusting and rearranging the furniture and said grumpily, "I don't understand why we have to entertain him. He could stay in the hotel."

"It will be interesting to have him here," Mina said.

"Interesting!"

Mina's father, overhearing the conversation, said, "It's good for Mina to meet such a famous man. He'll be an inspiration to her." Usually stern, he smiled at Mina now. "You're the only daughter I have who cares about reading and learning. I want you to come in when he's here and talk to him."

On the day of his arrival, Mina and Simin walked back from school together to Mina's house, wearing their new dresses instead of the gray uniforms. Right after school they had changed. They each had bought a hard-cover copy of Ardavani's latest book for him to autograph.

"Do you think it's worth it?" Simin asked.

"What?"

"Meeting him."

"What are you talking about?"

"It's just that...it makes me so nervous."

The owner of the barber shop underneath Mina's house was standing on the sidewalk in front of his store. He waved at Mina and said, "I gave your father a haircut today."

Mina smiled. She and Simin went through the back door and up the stairs that led to a row of rooms. One was used as a living room, one as an office by Mina's father, and one belonged to Mina.

They crossed the veranda to Mina's room. They had not encountered anyone on the way and the ceiling fans, going in every room, muffled most sounds. They sat there on hard-backed chairs and waited. A soft knock sounded at the door and Mina's father came in. He had on the dark suit he always wore when he went to court, and a polka-dot maroon and white tie. His graying hair was neatly combed and his face looked jovial.

"Don't you two ever get tired of chattering? Yap, yap, yap—that's all you do." He laughed.

Simin smiled at him politely.

"How would you like to come and meet Mahmood Ardavani? He's waiting to meet you, the two prettiest and smartest girls in the city."

"Now?" Mina asked.

"Now." He walked away. They followed slowly, carrying the books.

Mahmood Ardavani was sitting on the green and gold silk sofa in a corner of the living room, holding a glass of *sharbat*. Mina's father sat next to him with a glass of *sharbat* also. The rose scent of the drink filled the air.

The dining room table was set, with plates and glasses upside down so they would not catch the dirt from the street.

Mahmood Ardavani put down his glass and got up as Mina and Simin entered. He was friendly and at ease and looked very much like his photographs. He wore casual clothes—a blue and white shirt and denim pants. Mina's father made the introductions.

Mina and Simin were silent. The things Mina had prepared to say, such as, "I've always admired your work," or "I'm pleased to be in the presence of such a great writer," escaped her. She glanced toward the window at the dentist who had his office above the bank across the street. The dentist was bending over, working on a man's teeth.

"I'm so happy to meet you, after having read so much of your work," she finally said to Ardavani. She detected a tremor deep inside, and felt transformed just being in his presence; the air around her had a new intensity.

"Thank you. I'm very flattered," Ardavani said, raising his hand to shake hers.

Then he turned to Simin and shook hands with her. Simin blushed. Mina noticed they held each others' hands for a moment before letting go. He stared into Simin's eyes for a long time, his gaze as penetrating as in his photographs.

"You two are classmates?" he asked.

"Yes. I've always admired your work," Simin said.

"I am so pleased to know that lovely girls like you are my readers."

Simin raised the book she was holding and said, "I brought this for you to autograph."

He smiled and nodded his head. Then suddenly, as if he had awakened from a dream, he took his eyes off her and turned to Mina.

"I see you have a copy of the same book. Shall I autograph both of them?"

Mina nodded.

He took the books and, sitting down with them, thought for a moment. "I'll improvise a poem for each of you."

"Oh, wonderful," Mina said, the words just flowing out of her.

He began to write something in one book and then the other. Then he gave the books back to them. "Do me a favor. Don't read them now. Save them for later."

Simin and Mina nodded.

"Sit down. Tell me, what other things do you read?"

The two girls sank onto the silk-covered loveseat.

"We read Hafiz and Saadi for school," Simin said. "And Mina and I read almost everything printed in the *Teheran Monthly* and *Setareh*."

"Very good. What are you two girls going to do when you graduate from high school?"

"I don't know," Simin said.

"I don't know either," Mina remarked.

"I hope to send my daughter to the university," Mina's father said.

Mina wanted to bring up the idea of being sent abroad but Ardavani's presence was inhibiting. Anyway, it did not seem to matter that much at the moment.

They talked for a few more minutes and then Mina's father said, "Mr. Ardavani and I have a lot of business that we want to discuss." He looked at the set table. "In fact I'm sorry to say he won't be able to eat with us here tonight. We'll have to meet someone else, a mutual friend."

Mina and then Simin got up and stood staring at Ardavani.

He smiled at them. "I'm happy to have had the pleasure of meeting you."

"I am too," Mina said.

"So am I," Simin said.

They turned around and left. Mina's father was laughing at something that Ardavani was saying in a low voice.

The girls began to run toward Mina's room as soon as they reached the veranda. As soon as they got into the room, they opened the books.

For Mina he had written: "One morning I woke and realized I was in love with a dark-eyed, dark-haired girl with a mole on her upper lip. Now every time I see a girl looking like that I recall that faraway love and fall in love again."

For Simin he had written: "Your ethereal beauty will always remain food for the imagination of the poet."

"He liked you better than me," Simin said.

"Yours sounds better to me, more grand."

Simin shook her head. "It's so impersonal."

"He kept his eyes on you almost the whole time."

Simin shrugged.

They hardly spoke about their impressions of him. In a few moments Simin left. Mina did not sleep well that night. She tossed and turned and got out of the bed a few times and looked outside. The night air was crisp and the sky crowded with innumerable stars. She could see that the room where Ardavani slept was lighted and she wondered if he was reading or had fallen asleep with the light on. She wished she could tiptoe over to his room and sit by his bedside and talk.

The next morning she would have to get up early and leave for school, probably before he got up.

As soon as she returned to bed she felt anxious and was restless again. It wasn't just the meeting with Ardavani that had shaken her. It was Simin's manner too. She had seemed so humorless as they compared the poems.

At school Simin seemed cool and distant. All day she kept to herself. At recess Mina saw her sitting alone on the veranda, staring into space. She went over and tried to talk to her but Simin barely looked at her. Her eyes seemed to be focused on a landscape that Mina no longer shared. After classes Mina looked for Simin, but she had left without waiting for her as she almost always did. Mina walked home despondent.

Two months later, on a holiday, Mina went to a picnic in a park outside of the city.

The park was crowded with many families, their children swinging on ropes they had tied to trees or jumping over rivulets of water. Women were cooking on portable stoves or fires they had built with sticks.

Mina walked away from her family to a quieter section, and she was startled to see Simin standing by a little stream with a fishing pole in her hand. She had rarely been alone with Simin since Ardavani's visit. Simin had persisted in keeping to herself, more or less ignoring her. It was near dusk and the air had a reddish tinge. Simin's face looked flushed and grave. She wore the dress they had had made for Mahmood Ardavani's visit. Mina walked over very quietly, and standing behind her, whispered, "Simin."

Simin turned around and looked at her dreamily for an instant. "Oh, you!" She grabbed Mina's hand instinctively and then let go.

"I'm so glad to find you here. I've been bored all day," Mina said.

"Where's your family?"

"Over there."

"Mine are on that side. That's why we didn't run into each other before." Simin raised the rod, lifting the hook from the water, and abandoned it on the ground. "I have to sit down. I'm tired."

She sat on the grassy bank of the stream and Mina sat next to her. Mosquitoes buzzed in the trees that stood sparsely around them. The air had a slightly rotting smell.

"Tell me, why have you been avoiding me?" Mina asked after a few moments of silence.

"Oh, no reason."

"Please tell me."

Simin, holding her head so that all Mina could see was her profile, said, "You must know. It was what happened that day with Ardavani, what he wrote for you coming spontaneously from him. I envied you so much for it. I just had to avoid you until the feelings passed." Her voice sounded hollow and faraway. Mina felt a chill listening to that voice which was almost unrecognizable.

"Oh, that's so silly," she managed to say.

"When we were in the room with him, I wished so much for you to be out of the room—you and your father. I wanted so badly to be alone with Ardavani," Simin went on.

Mina recalled that she had had similar thoughts when she stood in the room and felt ignored by Ardavani. But the thoughts had quickly vanished, like sparks. She lowered her head so that Simin could not see the tears that had come into her eyes.

"All that is past now," she said after a moment. She was hopeful for an instant, but the next moment she could see that the gap that had begun to open between them was only deepening. The confession had made it worse instead of better. A grayness, denser than ever before, enveloped her.

from
The Lords of Discipline

B Y

P A T

C O N R O Y

Will: I've always been interested in girls, but that doesn't mean I can talk to them unless I know them really well. I've always thought girls would like me if they ever got to know me. You know, that wonderful sensitive guy I'm convinced I am. I always thought that they would love me if they could get past my sarcasm and my fear of them. This girl got past it all. Her name was Annie Kate Gervais, Mark. Isn't that a beautiful name? I let down all the defenses for her. I thought about her every moment. I felt alive thinking about her, on fire. I was on fire when I was away from her, too, Mark, but it was a different kind of fire. I told Annie Kate things I had never told anybody. I felt handsome around her. For the first time in my whole life, I felt handsome. I'd look in the mirror and I'd feel good about the way I looked. She changed me completely, Mark, and I'll never be the same person I was before. I'll never be happy until I feel that way about someone again and she feels the same about me. But she left me and I'm sure I'll never see her or hear from her again. See, I was sure she loved me as much as I did her. I was sure she dreamed about me as much as I dreamed about her. But I was wrong, Mark. I was wrong about that just like I've been wrong about everything else this year. I can't even look at her house now. I can't go to the places where we walked. I hurt every time I think about her. I'm afraid I won't ever find that again. And I feel ugly again, so ugly that I can't stand it.

The Bride

BY

SUNITI

NAMJOSHI

nce upon a time there was a proud young prince, and he had reason to be proud. He was heir to the kingdom, he was handsome and healthy, he had been extremely well educated, and all the social graces that could reasonably be taught had been carefully inculcated. What was more, his father was a king, and his father's father, and his father before that, so that his right to rule was undisputed. Now, when it was time for this young man to marry, he said to his father, "Father, you have always said that only the best was fit for me. I have the best falcons, and the best hounds and the best stallions in all the world. But where will you find a bride who is worthy of me?" The king didn't think that this would be much of a problem. He had contests instituted throughout the kingdom. There were contests for beauty, and contests for strength, and contests for knowledge and intelligence and wit, and there were skill-testing contests for all sorts of things such as archery and music. When the tests were done, the winners of the contests were presented to the prince. He looked them over. Their credentials were good. Indeed, he began to be afraid that some of their credentials were better than his. "These women have excelled," he said to his father, "but they seem to be lacking in the womanly qualities." "Well, of course," said his father. "I have weeded these out. You can now choose from those who did not compete."

The Darling

~

BY

ANTON

CHEKHOV

 lenka, the daughter of the retired collegiate assessor Plemyannikov, was sitting on the little porch that faced the courtyard, lost in thought. It was hot, the flies were annoyingly persistent, and it was pleasant to think that it would soon be evening. Dark rain clouds were gathering from the east, bringing with them an occasional breath of moisture.

Kukin, a theater manager who ran an amusement garden known as the Tivoli, and who lodged in the wing of the house, was standing in the middle of the courtyard staring up at the sky.

"Again!" he said in despair. "It's going to rain again! Every day it rains; every day, as if to spite me! I might just as well put a noose around my neck! It's ruin! Every day terrible losses!"

He clasped his hands, turned to Olenka and went on. "That's our life for you, Olga Semyonovna. It's enough to make you weep! You work, you do your very best, you worry and lose sleep, always thinking how to make it better—and what happens? On the one hand, the public is ignorant, barbarous. I give them the very best operetta, a pantomime, magnificent vaudeville artists—but do you think that's what they want? Do you think they understand it? What they want is slapstick! Give them trash! And then, look at the weather! Rain almost every evening. It started the tenth of May and it's been raining incessantly ever since—all May and June. Simply dreadful! The public doesn't come, but I still have to pay the rent, don't I—and the artists?"

The next day toward evening the clouds again appeared, and, laughing hysterically, Kukin said, "Well, go on, rain! Flood the whole park, drown me! Bad luck to me in this world and the next! Let the artists sue me! Let them send me to prison—to Siberia—to the scaffold! Ha! Ha! Ha!"

And the third day it was the same....

Olenka listened to Kukin gravely, silently, and sometimes tears would come into her eyes. She was so moved by his misfortunes that she ended by falling in love with him. He was an emaciated little man with a yellow face and hair combed down over his temples; he spoke in a thin tenor voice, twisting his mouth to one side, and despair was permanently engraved on his face; nevertheless, he aroused a deep and genuine feeling in her. She was always in love with someone and could not live otherwise. First it had been her papa, who was now ill and sat in an armchair in a darkened room, breathing with difficulty; then it had been her aunt, who used to come from Bryansk every other year; and before that, when she was at school, she had been in love with her French teacher. She was a quiet, good-natured, compassionate girl with meek, gentle eyes and very good health. At the sight of her full, rosy cheeks, her soft, white neck with a dark little mole on it, and the kind, ingenuous smile that came over her face when she listened to anything pleasant, men thought, "Yes, not bad!" and smiled too, while the ladies present could not refrain from suddenly seizing her hand in the middle of a conversation and exclaiming in an outburst of delight, "You darling!"

The house she had lived in since birth, and which, according to her father's will, was to be hers, was located on the outskirts of the city on Gypsy Road, not far from the Tivoli. In the evenings and at night when she heard the band playing and skyrockets exploding, it seemed to her that it was Kukin at war with his fate, assaulting his chief enemy, the apathetic public; then her heart melted, she had no desire to sleep, and when he returned home at daybreak she would tap softly at her bedroom window and, letting him see only her face and one shoulder through the curtain, would smile tenderly at him....

He proposed to her and they were married. And when he had a good look at her neck and her plump, fine shoulders, he clapped his hands together and exclaimed, "Darling!"

He was happy, but as it rained both the day and the night of the wedding, his expression of despair remained unchanged.

They got on well together. She presided over the box office, looked after things in the garden, kept the accounts and paid the salaries; and her rosy cheeks, her sweet, artless smile, shone now in the box-office window, now in the wings of the theater, now at the buffet. She began telling her friends that the most remarkable, the most important and essential thing in the whole world was the theater—that only through the theater could one derive true pleasure and become a cultivated and humane person.

"But do you suppose the public understands that?" she would ask. "What it wants is slapstick!" Yesterday we gave *Faust Inside Out,* and almost every box was empty, but if Vanichka and I had put on some kind of trash, then, believe me, the theater would have been packed. Tomorrow Vanichka and I are putting on *Orpheus in Hell.* Do come."

Whatever Kukin said about the theater and the actors she repeated. Like him she despised the public for its ignorance and indifference to art; she took a hand in the rehearsals, correcting the actors, kept an eye on the conduct of the musicians, and when there was an unfavorable notice in the local newspaper, shed tears, and then went to the editor for an explanation.

The actors loved her and called her "Vanichka and I" and "the darling." She was sorry for them and used to lend them small sums of money, and if they deceived her she wept in secret but did not complain to her husband.

They got on well in the winter too. They leased the municipal theater for the season and sublet it for short periods to a Ukrainian troupe, a magician, or a local dramatic club. Olenka grew plumper and was always beaming with satisfaction, while Kukin grew thinner and yellower and complained of terrible losses, although business was not bad during the winter. He coughed at night and she would give him an infusion of raspberries and linden blossoms, rub him with eau de Cologne, and wrap him in her soft shawls.

"What a sweet precious you are!" she would say with perfect sincerity, as she stroked his hair. "My handsome pet!"

At Lent he went to Moscow to gather a new troupe, and without him she could not sleep, but sat all night at the window looking at the stars. She likened herself to the hens, which also stay awake all night and are uneasy when the cock is not in the henhouse. Kukin was detained in Moscow, wrote that he would return by Easter, and in his letters sent instructions regarding the Tivoli. But on the Monday of Passion Week, late in the evening, there was a sudden, ominous knocking at the gate; someone was hammering at the wicket as if it were a barrel—boom! boom! boom! The sleepy cook, splashing through the puddles in her bare feet, ran to open the gate.

"Open, please!" said someone on the other side of the gate in a deep bass voice. "There is a telegram for you!"

Olenka had received telegrams from her husband before, but this time for some reason she felt numb with fright. She opened the telegram with trembling hands and read:

IVAN PETROVICH DIED SUDDENLY TODAY AWAITING THISD INSTRUCTIONS FUFUNERAL TUESDAY.

That was exactly the way the telegram had it: "fufuneral" and the incomprehensible "thisd"; it was signed by the director of the operetta company.

"My precious!" Olenka sobbed. "Vanichka, my precious, my dearest! Why did we ever meet? Why did I know you and love you? Whom can your poor forsaken Olenka turn to now?"

Kukin was buried on Tuesday in the Vagankovo cemetery in Moscow. Olenka returned home on Wednesday, and as soon as she reached her room sank onto the bed and sobbed so loudly that she could be heard in the street and in the neighboring courtyards.

"The darling!" said the neighbors, crossing themselves. "Darling Olga Semyonovna! Poor soul, how she grieves!"

Three months later Olenka was returning from mass one day, in deep mourning and very sad. It happened that one of her neighbors, Vasily Andreich Pustovalov, the manager of Babakayev's lumberyard, was also returning from church and walked with her. He wore a straw hat, a white waistcoat with a gold watch chain, and looked more like a landowner than a merchant.

"Everything happens as it is ordained, Olga Semyonovna," he said gravely, with a note of sympathy in his voice, "and if one of our dear ones passes on, we must take ourselves in hand and bear it submissively."

Having seen Olenka to her gate, he said good-bye and went on. All day long she seemed to hear his grave voice, and as soon as she closed her eyes she dreamed of his dark beard. She liked him very much. And apparently she had made an impression on him too, because not long afterwards an elderly lady whom she scarcely knew came to have coffee with her, and as soon as she was seated at the table began to talk of Pustovalov, saying that he was a fine steady man and that any marriageable woman would be happy to marry him. Three days later Pustovalov himself paid her a visit. He did not stay long, not more than ten minutes, and said little, but Olenka fell in love with him—she was so much in love that she lay awake all night, inflamed as with a fever, and in the morning she sent for the elderly lady. The betrothal was arranged, and the wedding followed soon afterwards.

After they were married Pustovalov and Olenka got on very well together. As a rule he was in the lumberyard till dinnertime, then he went out on business and Olenka took his place and sat in the office till evening, making out bills and dispatching orders.

"Every year the price of lumber rises twenty per cent," she would say to customers and acquaintances. "Why, we used to deal in local timber, but now Vasichka has to travel to the province of Mogilev every year for wood. And the freight!" she would add, covering her cheeks with her hands in horror. "The freight!"

It seemed to her that she had been in the lumber business for ages and ages, that lumber was the most important and essential thing in life, and she found something touching, dear to her, in such words as girder, beam, plank, batten, boxboard, lath, scantling, slab.... At night she would dream of whole mountains of boards and planks, long endless caravans of wagons carrying lumber to some distant place; she dreamed of a whole regiment of 8-inch beams 28 feet long standing on end, marching on the lumberyard, beams, girders, slabs, striking against one another with the hollow sound of dry wood, all falling, then rising, piling themselves one upon another.... When she cried out in her sleep Pustovalov would speak to her tenderly, saying, "Olenka, what's the matter, darling? Cross yourself!"

Whatever ideas her husband had became her own. If he thought the room was hot or business was slow, she thought so too. Her husband did not care for entertainment of any kind, and on holidays stayed at home, and so did she.

"You are always at home or in the office," her friends said to her. "You ought to go to the theater, darling, or to the circus."

"Vasichka and I have no time for the theater," she would reply sedately. "We are working people, we're not interested in such foolishness. What's the good of those theaters?"

On Saturday evenings they would go to vespers, on holidays to early mass, and as they walked home side by side their faces reflected the emotion of the service. There was an agreeable aroma about them both, and her silk dress rustled pleasantly. At home they had tea and buns with various kinds of jam, and afterwards a pie. Every day at noon, in the yard and beyond the gate in the street, there was a delicious smell of borsch and roast lamb or duck and, on fast days, fish; no one could pass their gate without feeling hungry. In the office the samovar was always boiling and the customers were treated to tea and cracknels. Once a week they went to the baths and returned side by side, both very red.

"Yes, everything goes well with us, thank God," Olenka would say to her friends. "I wish everyone were as happy as Vasichka and I."

When Pustovalov went to the province of Mogilev to buy timber, she missed him dreadfully, and lay awake nights crying. Sometimes in the evening Smirnin, a young army veterinarian to whom they rented the wing of the house, came to see her. They chatted or played cards, and this diverted her. She was especially interested in what he told her of his domestic life. He was married and had a son, but was separated from his wife because she had been unfaithful to him, and now he hated her; he sent her forty rubles a month for the support of the child. Listening to all this, Olenka sighed, shook her head, and was sorry for him.

"Well, God keep you," she would say, accompanying him to the stairs with a candle. "Thank you for passing the time with me, and may the Queen of Heaven give you health."

She always expressed herself in this grave, circumspect manner in imitation of her husband. Just as the veterinarian was about to disappear behind the door below, she would call to him and say, "You know, Vladimir Platonych, you ought to make it up with your wife. For your son's sake, you should forgive her! The little fellow probably understands everything!"

When Pustovalov returned she would tell him in a low voice all about the veterinarian and his unhappy life, and they both would sigh, shake their heads, and talk about the little boy, who very likely missed his father. Then, by some strange association of ideas, they both stood before the ikons, bowed to the ground, and prayed that God would send them children.

Thus the Pustovalovs lived quietly and peaceably, in love and complete harmony for six years. Then one winter day, after drinking hot tea in the office, Vasily Andreich went out without his cap to dispatch some lumber, caught cold, and was taken ill. He was treated by the best doctors, but the illness had its way with him, and after four months he died. And again Olenka was a widow.

"Whom can I turn to, my darling?" she sobbed, after burying her husband. "How can I live without you, miserable and unhappy as I am? Good people, pity me!"

She went about in a black dress with weepers, gave up wearing a hat and gloves for good, seldom went out of the house except to go to church or to visit her husband's grave, and at home she lived like a nun. Only after six months did she take off her widow's weeds and open the shutters of her windows. Occasionally she was seen in the mornings, going with her cook to the market, but how she lived and what went on in her house could only be surmised. People based their conjectures on the fact that she was seen drinking tea in her garden with the veterinarian, that he read the newspaper aloud to her, and that, on meeting an acquaintance in the post office, she said, "There is no proper veterinary inspection in our city, and that's why there is so much sickness around. You often hear of people getting ill from milk or catching infections from horses and cows. The health of domestic animals ought to be just as well looked after as the health of human beings."

She repeated the ideas of the veterinarian, and now was of the same opinion as he about everything. It was clear that she could not live even a year without some attachment, and had found new happiness in the wing of her own house. Another woman would have been censured for this, but no one could think ill of Olenka; everything about her was so natural. Neither she nor the veterinarian spoke to anyone of the change in their relations, and tried, indeed, to conceal it, but they did not succeed because Olenka could not keep a secret. When his regimental colleagues visited him, while she poured tea for them or served supper she would talk of the cattle plague, the pearl disease, the municipal slaughterhouses. He would be dreadfully embarrassed, and when the guests had gone, would seize her by the arm and hiss angrily, "I've asked you before not to talk about things you don't understand! When we veterinarians are talking among ourselves, please don't interfere! It's really annoying!"

She would look at him in amazement and anxiously inquire, "But, Volodochka, what am I to talk about?" Then, with tears in her eyes, she would embrace him, begging him not to be angry, and they were both happy.

This happiness did not last long. The veterinarian went away with his regiment, went away forever, as the regiment was transferred to some distant place—it may even have been Siberia. And Olenka was left alone.

Now she was quite alone. Her father had died long ago; his armchair lay in the attic, covered with dust and with one leg missing. She grew thin and plain, and when people met her in the street they did not glance at her and smile as they used to; clearly, her best years were over and behind her, and now a new, uncertain life was beginning, one that did not bear thinking of. In the evening, as she sat on her porch, Olenka could hear the band playing and skyrockets going off at the Tivoli, but this no longer called up anything to her mind. She gazed indifferently into her empty courtyard, thought of nothing, wished for nothing, and later, when darkness fell, she went to bed and dreamed of the empty courtyard. She ate and drank as though involuntarily.

Above all—and worst of all—she no longer had any opinions whatever. She saw objects about her, understood what was going on, but could not form an opinion about anything and did not know what to talk about. And how awful it is to have no opinions! You see a bottle, for instance, or rain, or a peasant driving a cart, but what the bottle, the rain, or the peasant may be for, what the significance of them is, you cannot say, and could not even for a thousand rubles. When Kukin was with her, or Pustovalov, or later, the veterinarian, Olenka could explain everything, could express an opinion on anything you like, but now there was the same emptiness in her mind and heart as in the courtyard. It was painful, and bitter as wormwood in the mouth.

Little by little the town was spreading in all directions; Gypsy Road was now a street, and where the gardens of the Tivoli and the lumberyards had been, houses sprang up and lanes formed. How swiftly time passes! Olenka's house grew shabby, the roof was rusty, the shed sloped, and the whole yard was overgrown with tall grass and prickly nettles. Olenka herself had aged and grown plain; in the summer she sat on the porch, and her soul was empty, bleak, and bitter; in the winter she sat at the window and stared at the snow. There were times when a breath of spring or the sound of church bells brought to her on the wind would suddenly provoke a rush of memories; then her heart melted, her eyes brimmed with tears, but this lasted only a moment, and there was again emptiness and uncertainty as to the purpose of life. Bryska, the black kitten, rubbed against her, purring softly, but Olenka was not affected by these feline caresses. Was that what she needed? She wanted a love that would take possession of her whole soul, her mind, that would give her ideas, a direction in life, that would warm her old blood. She shook the black kitten off her lap and said irritably, "Get away! Go on! There's nothing for you here!"

And so it was, day after day, year after year, no joy whatsoever, no opinions of any sort. Whatever Mavra the cook said, she accepted.

One hot July day, toward evening, when the cattle were being driven home and the whole yard was filled with clouds of dust, someone unexpectedly knocked at the gate. Olenka went to open it herself and was astounded at what she saw: there stood Smirnin, the veterinarian, his hair gray, and in civilian dress. All at once, she remembered everything and, unable to control herself, burst into tears, dropping her head onto his breast without a word. She was so moved that she scarcely was aware of going into the house and sitting down to tea with him.

"My dear!" she murmured, trembling with joy. "Vladimir Platonych! What brings you here?"

"I have come here for good," he said. "I've retired from the army and I want to settle down and try my luck on my own. And besides, it's time for my son to go to high school. He's growing up. I am reconciled with my wife, you know."

"Where is she?" asked Olenka.

"She's at the hotel with the boy, and I'm out looking for lodgings."

"Good heavens, my dear, take my house! Lodgings! Goodness, I wouldn't take any rent for it," cried Olenka, growing excited and weeping again. "You live here, and the wing will do for me. Heavens, how glad I am!"

The next day they began painting the roof and whitewashing the walls, and Olenka, with her arms akimbo, walked about the yard giving orders. Her face beamed with her old smile, and she was animated and fresh, as though she had waked from a long sleep. The veterinarian's wife arrived, thin and homely, with short hair and a capricious expression. With her came the little boy, Sasha, small for his age (he was going on ten), chubby, with bright blue eyes and dimples in his cheeks. No sooner had he entered the courtyard than he began chasing the cat, and immediately his gay and joyous laughter could be heard.

"Auntie, is that your cat?" he asked Olenka. "When she has little ones, please give us one of her kittens. Mama is terribly afraid of mice."

Olenka talked to him, gave him tea, and her heart grew suddenly warm and there was a sweet ache in her bosom, as if this little boy were her own son. In the evening when he sat in the dining room doing his homework, she gazed at him with tenderness and pity as she whispered, "My darling, my pretty one.... How clever you are, my little one, and so fair!"

"An island," he read aloud from the book, "is a body of land entirely surrounded by water."

"An island is a body of land..." she repeated, and this was the first opinion she had uttered with conviction after years of silence and emptiness of mind.

She now had opinions of her own, and at supper she talked to Sasha's parents about how difficult the lessons were for children in the high school, but that, nevertheless, a classical education was better than a technical course, because it opened all avenues—you could be a doctor...and engineer....

Sasha started going to high school. His mother went to Kharkov to visit her sister and did not come back; his father used to go away every day to inspect herds, and he sometimes was away for three days together. It seemed to Olenka that Sasha was quite forsaken, that he was unwanted, that he was being starved to death, and she moved him into the wing with her and settled him in a little room there.

For six months now Sasha has been living in her wing. Every morning Olenka goes into his room where he lies fast asleep, his hand under his cheek, breathing quietly. She is always sorry to wake him.

"Sashenka," she says sadly, "get up, darling. It's time for school."

He gets up, dresses, says his prayers, and sits down to breakfast; he drinks three glasses of tea, eats two large cracknels and half a buttered roll. He is still not quite awake and consequently ill-humored.

"Now, Sashenka, you have not learned your fable very well," Olenka says, gazing at him as if she were seeing him off on a long journey. "You are such a worry to me! You must do your best, darling; you must study.... Pay attention to your teachers!"

"Oh, leave me alone, please!" he says.

Then he walks down the street to school, a little figure in a big cap, with a knapsack on his back. Olenka silently follows him.

"Sashenka–a!" she calls. And when he looks around she thrusts a date or a caramel into his hand. When they turn in to the school lane he feels ashamed of being followed by a tall, stout lady; he looks back and says, "You'd better go home, Auntie. I can go alone now."

She stops, but does not take her eyes off him until he has disappeared into the school entrance. Ah, how she loves him! Not one of her former attachments had been so deep; never before had her soul surrendered itself so devotedly and with such joy as now, when her maternal feelings have been quickened. For this little boy who is not her own, for the dimples in his cheeks, for his cap, she would give her whole life, would give it with joy and tears of tenderness. Why? But who knows why?

Having seen Sasha off to school she goes quietly home, contented, serene, full of love; her face, grown younger in the last six months, beams with joy; people meeting her look at her with pleasure and say, "Good morning Olga Semyonova, darling. How are you, darling?"

"The lessons is school are so difficult nowadays," she says, as she goes about her marketing. "It's no joke. Yesterday in the first class they gave him a fable to learn by heart, a Latin translation, and a problem.... You know, it's too much for the little fellow."

And she begins talking about the teachers, the lessons, the textbooks—saying just what Sasha says about them.

At three o'clock they have dinner together; in the evening they do the homework together, and cry. When she puts him to bed she takes a long time making the sign of the cross over him and whispering a prayer. Then she goes to bed and dreams of that faraway, misty future when Sasha, having finished his studies, will become a doctor or an engineer, will have a large house of his own, horses, a carriage, when he will marry and have children of his own.... She falls asleep, still thinking of the same thing, and the tears run down her cheeks from under closed eyelids, while the black cat lies beside her purring: mrr...mrr...mrr....

Suddenly there is a loud knock at the gate and Olenka wakes up, breathless with fear, her heart pounding. Half a minute later there is another knock.

"It's a telegram from Kharkov," she thinks, her whole body trembling. "Sasha's mother is sending for him.... Oh, Lord!"

She is in despair, her head, hands, and feet are cold, and it seems to her that she is the most unfortunate woman in the whole world. But another moment passes, she hears voices: it is the veterinarian coming home from the club.

"Well, thank God!" she thinks. Gradually the weight on her heart lifts, and she feels relieved; she goes back to bed and thinks of Sasha, who is fast asleep in the next room, sometimes crying out in his sleep, "I'll give it to you! Go on! No fighting!"

Day of the Bride

~

BY

JOY

KOGAWA

The day of the bride dawns
Through layers of white plaster skin
And multi-sashed kimono
Head made huge by lacquered hair—
She is swept ashore in her glass bottle
White and tight as a folded paper message
Eyes hidden in a swirl of green boughs.
She moves like a mannequin
Manoeuvred by centuries of ceremony
Under the weight of speech and incantation
A wail of priests and watching families
Beside rows of low tables
With small triangles of paper
Congratulatory slits of squid and curls of seaweed.
Then kneeling at the bend of a fresh memory
She is discarded by her heavy day
And is plunged into the twentieth century
Tiny apartment daily stream
As a barely visible
Folded paper speck

from

Life After God

~

BY

DOUGLAS
COUPLAND

ow: I am an affectionate man but I have much trouble showing it.

When I was younger I used to worry so much about being alone—of
being unlovable or incapable of love. As the years went on, my worries
changed. I worried that I had become incapable of having a
relationship, of offering intimacy. I felt as though the world lived inside
a warm house at night and I was outside, and I couldn't be seen—
because I was out there in the night. But now I am inside that house
and it feels just the same.

Being alone here now, all of my old fears are erupting—the fears I
thought I had buried forever by getting married: fear of loneliness;
fear that being in and out of love too many times itself makes you
harder to love; fear that I would never experience real love; fear that
someone would fall in love with me, get extremely close, learn
everything about me and then pull the plug; fear that love is only
important up until a certain point after which everything is negotiable.

For so many years I lived a life of solitude and I thought life was fine. But I knew that unless I explored intimacy and shared intimacy with someone else then life would never progress beyond a certain point. I remember thinking that unless I knew what was going on inside of someone else's head other than my own I was going to explode.

My Father
Writes to
My Mother

~

BY

ASSIA

DJEBAR

henever my mother spoke of my father, she, in common with all
the women in her town, simply used the personal pronoun in
Arabic corresponding to "him." Thus, every time she used a
verb in the third person singular which didn't have a noun subject, she
was naturally referring to her husband. This form of speech was characteristic of every married woman, from fifteen to sixty, with the proviso
that in later years, if the husband had undertaken the pilgrimage to
Mecca, he could be given the title of "Hajj."

Everybody, children and adults, especially girls and women, since
all important conversations took place among the womenfolk, learnt
very quickly to adapt to this rule whereby a husband and wife must
never be referred to by name.

After she had been married for a few years, my mother gradually
learnt a little French. She was able to exchange a few halting words
with the wives of my father's colleagues who had, for the most part,
come from France and, like us, lived with their families in the little
block of flats set aside for the village teachers.

I don't know exactly when my mother began to say, '*My husband* has come, *my husband* has gone out...I'll ask *my husband*,' etc. Although my mother did make rapid progress in the language, in spite of taking it up fairly late in life, I can still hear the evident awkwardness in her voice betrayed by her laboured phraseology, her slow and deliberate enunciation at that time. Nevertheless, I can sense how much it cost her modesty to refer to my father directly in this way.

It was as if a floodgate had opened within her, perhaps in her relationship with her husband. Years later, during the summers we spent in her native town, when chatting in Arabic with her sisters or cousins, my mother would refer to him quite naturally by his first name, even with a touch of superiority. What a daring innovation! Yes, quite unhesitatingly—I was going to say, unequivocally—in any case, without any of the usual euphemisms and verbal circumlocutions. When her aunts and elderly female relations were present, she would once more use the traditional formalities, out of respect for them; such freedom of language would have appeared insolent and incongruous to the ears of the pious old ladies.

Years went by. As my mother's ability to speak French improved, while I was still a child of no more than twelve, I came to realise an irrefutable fact: namely that, in the face of all these womenfolk, my parents formed a couple. One thing was an even greater source of pride in me: when my mother referred to any of the day-to-day incidents in our village life—which in our city relatives' eyes was very backward—the tall figure of my father—my childhood hero—seemed to pop up in the midst of all these women engaged in idle chit-chat on the age-old patios to which they were confined.

My father, no one except my father; none of the other women ever saw fit to refer to their menfolk, their masters who spent the day outside the house and returned home in the evening, taciturn, with eyes on the ground. These nameless uncles, cousins, relatives by marriage, were for us an unidentifiable collection of individuals to all of whom their spouses alluded impartially in the masculine gender.

With the exception of my father...My mother, with lowered eyes, would calmly pronounce his name "Tahar"—which, I learned very early, meant "The Pure"—and even when a suspicion of a smile flickered across the other women's faces or they looked half ill at ease, half indulgent, I thought that a rare distinction lit up my mother's face.

These harem conversations ran their imperceptible course: my ears only caught those phrases which singled my mother out above the rest. Because she always made a point of bringing my father's name into these exchanges, he became for me still purer than his given name betokened.

One day something occurred which was a portent that their relationship would never be the same again—a commonplace enough event in any other society, but which was unusual to say the least with us: in the course of an exceptionally long journey away from home (to a neighbouring province, I think), my father wrote to my mother—yes, to my mother!

He sent her a postcard, with a short greeting written diagonally across it in his large, legible handwriting, something like 'Best wishes from this distant region' or possibly, 'I am having a good journey and getting to know an unfamiliar region' etc. and he signed it simply with his first name. I am sure that, at the time, he himself would not have dared add any more intimate formula above his signature, such as 'I am thinking of you,' or even less, 'Yours affectionately.' But, on the half of the card reserved for the address of the recipient, he had written 'Madame' followed by his own surname, with the possible addition—but here I'm not sure—of 'and children,' that is to say, we three, of whom I, then about ten years old, was the eldest....

The radical change in customs was apparent for all to see: my father had quite brazenly written his wife's name, in his own handwriting, on a postcard which was going to travel from one town to another, which was going to be exposed to so many masculine eyes, including eventually our village postman—a Muslim postman to boot—and, what is more, he had dared refer to her in the western manner as "Madame So-and-So..." whereas, no local man, poor or rich, ever referred to his wife and children in any other way than by the vague periphrasis: "the household."

So, my father had "written" to my mother. When she visited her family she mentioned this postcard, in the simplest possible words and tone of voice, to be sure. She was about to describe her husband's four or five days' absence from the village, explaining the practical problems this had posed: my father having to order the provisions just before he left, so that the shopkeepers could deliver them every morning; she was going to explain how hard it was for a city woman to be isolated in a village with very young children and cut off in this way… But the other women had interrupted, exclaiming, in the face of this new reality, this almost incredible detail:

"He wrote to you, *to you*?"

"He wrote his wife's name and the postman must have read it? Shame!"

"He could at least have addressed the card to his son, for the principle of the thing, even if his son is only seven or eight!"

My mother did not reply. She was probably pleased, flattered even, but she said nothing. Perhaps she was suddenly ill at ease, or blushing from embarrassment; yes, her husband had written to her, in person!… The eldest child, the only one who might have been able to read the card, was her daughter: so, daughter or wife, where was the difference as far as the addressee was concerned?

"I must remind you that I've learned to read French now!"

This postcard was, in fact, a most daring manifestation of affection. Her modesty suffered at that very moment that she spoke of it. Yet, it came second to her pride as a wife, which was secretly flattered.

The murmured exchanges of these segregated women struck a faint chord with me, as a little girl with observing eyes. And so, for the first time, I seem to have some intuition of the possible happiness, the mystery in the union of a man and a woman.

My father had dared "to write" to my mother. Both of them referred to each other by name, which was tantamount to declaring openly their love for each other, my father by writing to her, my mother by quoting my father henceforward without false shame in all her conversations.

Parlour Game

~

BY

ALDEN

NOWLAN

We were sitting there
hating one another when
some friends dropped in
who've always said
we're the most loving
couple they know

and of course the two of us
went into the act
as usual, each afraid
of the other's equally
strong inclination
to give the game away,

both sneering inwardly
for the first five or ten
minutes and then
both trying not to burst,
without knowing whether
the laughter that came
would be savage or joyous

—and within half an hour
we caught ourselves exchanging
silly and affectionate
smiles even when
nobody else was watching:

for the millionth time,
starting over again.

Seventeen Syllables

BY

HISAYE

YAMAMOTO

he first Rosie knew that her mother had taken to writing poems was one evening when she finished one and read it aloud for her daughter's approval. It was about cats, and Rosie pretended to understand it thoroughly and appreciate it no end, partly because she hesitated to disillusion her mother about the quantity and quality of Japanese she had learned in all the years now that she had been going to Japanese school every Saturday (and Wednesday, too, in the summer). Even so, her mother must have been skeptical about the depth of Rosie's understanding, because she explained afterwards about the kind of poem she was trying to write.

See, Rosie, she said, it was a *haiku*, a poem in which she must pack all her meaning into seventeen syllables only, which were divided into three lines of five, seven, and five syllables. In the one she had just read, she had tried to capture the charm of a kitten, as well as comment on the superstition that owning a cat of three colors meant good luck.

"Yes, yes, I understand. How utterly lovely," Rosie said, and her mother, either satisfied or seeing through the deception and resigned, went back to composing.

The truth was that Rosie was lazy; English lay ready on the tongue but Japanese had to be searched for and examined, and even then put forth tentatively (probably to meet with laughter). It was so much easier to say yes, yes, even when one meant no, no. Besides, this was what was in her mind to say: I was looking through one of your magazines from Japan last night, Mother, and towards the back I found some *haiku* in English that delighted me. There was one that made me giggle off and on until I fell asleep—

> It is morning, and lo!
> I lie awake, comme il faut,
> sighing for some dough.

Now, how to reach her mother, how to communicate the melancholy song? Rosie knew formal Japanese by fits and starts, her mother had even less English, no French. It was much more possible to say yes, yes.

It developed that her mother was writing the *haiku* for a daily newspaper, the *Mainichi Shimbun*, that was published in San Francisco. Los Angeles, to be sure, was closer to the farming community in which the Hayashi family lived and several Japanese vernaculars were printed there, but Rosie's parents said they preferred the tone of the northern paper. Once a week, the *Mainichi* would have a section devoted to *haiku*, and her mother became an extravagant contributor, taking for herself the blossoming pen name, Ume Hanazono.

So Rosie and her father lived for awhile with two women, her mother and Ume Hanazono. Her mother (Tome Hayashi by name) kept house, cooked, washed, and, along with her husband and the Carrascos, the Mexican family hired for the harvest, did her ample share of picking tomatoes out in the sweltering fields and boxing them in tidy strata in the cool packing shed. Ume Hanazono, who came to life after the dinner dishes were done, was an earnest, muttering stranger who often neglected speaking when spoken to and stayed busy at the parlor table as late as midnight scribbling with pencil on scratch paper or carefully copying characters on good paper with her fat, pale green Parker.

The new interest had some repercussions on the household routine. Before, Rosie had been accustomed to her parents and herself taking their hot baths early and going to bed almost immediately afterwards, unless her parents challenged each other to a game of flower cards or unless company dropped in. Now, if her father wanted to play cards, he had to resort to solitaire (at which he always cheated fearlessly), and if a group of friends came over, it was bound to contain someone who was also writing *haiku*, and the small assemblage would be split in two, her father entertaining the nonliterary members and her mother comparing ecstatic notes with the visiting poet.

If they went out, it was more of the same thing. But Ume Hanazono's life span, even for a poet's, was very brief—perhaps three months at most.

One night they went over to see the Hayano family in the neighboring town to the west, an adventure both painful and attractive to Rosie. It was attractive because there were four Hayano girls, all lovely and each one named after a season of the year (Haru, Natsu, Aki, Fuyu), painful because something had been wrong with Mrs. Hayano ever since the birth of her first child. Rosie would sometimes watch Mrs. Hayano, reputed to have been the belle of her native village, making her way about a room, stooped, slowly shuffling, violently trembling (*always* trembling), and she would be reminded that this woman, in this same condition, had carried and given issue to three babies. She would look wonderingly at Mr. Hayano, handsome, tall, and strong, and she would look at her four pretty friends. But it was not a matter she could come to any decision about.

On this visit, however, Mrs. Hayano sat all evening in the rocker, as motionless and unobtrusive as it was possible for her to be, and Rosie found the greater part of the evening practically anaesthetic. Too, Rosie spent most of it in the girls' room, because Haru, the garrulous one, said almost as soon as the bows and other greetings were over, "Oh, you must see my new coat!"

It was a pale plaid of grey, sand, and blue, with an enormous collar, and Rosie, seeing nothing special in it, said, "Gee, how nice."

"Nice?" said Haru, indignantly. "Is that all you can say about it? It's gorgeous! And so cheap, too. Only seventeen-ninety-eight, because it was a sale. The saleslady said it was twenty-five dollars regular."

"Gee," said Rosie, Natsu, who never said much and when she said anything said it shyly, fingered the coat covetously and Haru pulled it away.

"Mine," she said, putting it on. She minced in the aisle between two large beds and smiled happily. "Let's see how your mother likes it."

She broke into the front room and the adult conversation, and went to stand in front of Rosie's mother, while the rest watched from the door. Rosie's mother was properly envious. "May I inherit it when you're through with it?"

Haru, pleased, giggled and said yes, she could, but Natsu reminded gravely from the door, "You promised me, Haru."

Everyone laughed but Natsu, who shamefacedly retreated into the bedroom. Haru came in laughing, taking off the coat. "We were only kidding, Natsu," she said. "Here, you try it on now."

After Natsu buttoned herself into the coat, inspected herself solemnly in the bureau mirror, and reluctantly shed it, Rosie, Aki, and Fuyu got their turns, and Fuyu, who was eight, drowned in it while her sisters and Rosie doubled up in amusement. They all went into the front room later, because Haru's mother quaveringly called to her to fix the tea and rice cakes and open a can of sliced peaches for everybody. Rosie noticed that her mother and Mr. Hayano were talking together at the little table—they were discussing a *haiku* that Mr. Hayano was planning to send to the *Mainichi,* while her father was sitting at one end of the sofa looking through a copy of *Life*, the new picture magazine. Occasionally, her father would comment on a photograph, holding it toward Mrs. Hayano and speaking to her as he always did—loudly, as though he though someone such as she must surely be at least a trifle deaf also.

The five girls had their refreshments at the kitchen table, and it was while Rosie was showing the sisters her trick of swallowing peach slices without chewing (she chased each slippery crescent down with a swig of tea) that her father brought his empty teacup and untouched saucer to the sink and said, "Come on, Rosie, we're going home now."

"Already?" asked Rosie.

"Work tomorrow," he said.

He sounded irritated, and Rosie, puzzled, gulped one last yellow slice and stood up to go, while the sisters began protesting, as was their wont.

"We have to get up at five-thirty," he told them, going into the front room quickly, so that they did not have their usual chance to hang onto his hands and plead for an extension of time.

Rosie, following, saw that her mother and Mr. Hayano were sipping tea and still talking together, while Mrs. Hayano concentrated, quivering, on raising the handleless Japanese cup to her lips with both her hands and lowering it back to her lap. Her father, saying nothing, went out the door, onto the bright porch, and down the steps. Her mother looked up and asked, "Where is he going?"

"Where is he going?" Rosie said. "He said we were going home now."

"Going home?" Her mother looked with embarrassment at Mr. Hayano and his absorbed wife and then forced a smile. "He must be tired," she said.

Haru was not giving up yet. "May Rosie stay overnight?" she asked, and Natsu, Aki, and Fuyu came to reinforce their sister's plea by helping her make a circle around Rosie's mother. Rosie, for once, having no desire to stay, was relieved when her mother, apologizing to the perturbed Mr. and Mrs. Hayano for her father's abruptness at the same time, managed to shake her head no at the quartet, kindly but adamant, so that they broke their circle and let her go.

Rosie's father looked ahead into the windshield as the two joined him. "I'm sorry," her mother said. "You must be tired." Her father, stepping on the starter, said nothing. "You know how I get when it's *haiku*," she continued, "I forget what time it is." He only grunted.

As they rode homeward silently, Rosie, sitting between, felt a rush of hate for both, for her mother for begging, for her father for denying her mother. I wish this old Ford would crash, right now, she thought, then immediately, no, no, I wish my father would laugh, but it was too late: already the vision had passed through her mind of the green pick-up crumpled in the dark against one of the mighty eucalyptus trees they were just riding past, of the three contorted, bleeding bodies, one of them hers.

Rosie ran between two patches of tomatoes, her heart working more rambunctiously than she had ever known it to. How lucky it was that Aunt Taka and Uncle Gimpachi had come tonight, though, how very lucky. Otherwise, she might not have really kept her half-promise to meet Jesus Carrasco. Jesus, who was going to be a senior in September at the same school she went to, and his parents were the ones helping with the tomatoes this year. She and Jesus, who hardly remembered seeing each other at Cleveland High, where there were so many other people and two whole grades between them, had become great friends this summer—he always had a joke for her when he periodically drove the loaded pick-up up from the fields to the shed where she was usually sorting while her mother and father did the packing, and they laughed a great deal together over infinitesimal repartee during the afternoon break for chilled watermelon or ice cream in the shade of the shed.

What she enjoyed most was racing him to see which could finish picking a double row first. He, who could work faster, would tease her by slowing down until she thought she would surely pass him this time, then speeding up furiously to leave her several sprawling vines behind. Once he had made her screech hideously by crossing over, while her back was turned, to place atop the tomatoes in her green-stained bucket a truly monstrous, pale green worm (it had looked more like an infant snake). And it was when they had finished a contest this morning, after she had pantingly pointed a green finger at the immature tomatoes evident in the lugs at the end of his row and he had returned the accusation (with justice), that he had startlingly brought up the matter of their possible meeting outside the range of both their parents' dubious eyes.

"What for?" she had asked.

"I've got a secret I want to tell you," he said.

"Tell me now," she demanded.

"It won't be ready till tonight," he said.

She laughed. "Tell me tomorrow then."

"It'll be gone tomorrow," he threatened.

"Well, for seven hakes, what is it?" she had asked, more than twice, and when he had suggested that the packing shed would be an appropriate place to find out, she had cautiously answered maybe. She had not been certain she was going to keep the appointment until the arrival of her mother's sister and her husband. Their coming seemed a sort of signal of permission, of grace, and she had definitely made up her mind to lie and leave as she was bowing them welcome.

So, as soon as everyone appeared settled back for the evening, she announced loudly that she was going to the privy outside, "I'm going to the *benjo*!" and slipped out the door. And now that she was actually on her way, her heart pumped in such an undisciplined way that she could hear it with her ears. It's because I'm running, she told herself, slowing to a walk. The shed was up ahead, one more patch away, in the middle of the fields. Its bulk, looming in the dimness, took on a sinisterness that was funny when Rosie reminded herself that it was only a wooden frame with a canvas roof and three canvas walls that made a slapping noise on breezy days.

Jesus was sitting on the narrow plank that was the sorting platform and she went around to the other side and jumped backwards to seat herself on the rim of a packing stand. "Well, tell me," she said, without greeting, thinking her voice sounded reassuringly familiar.

"I saw you coming out the door," Jesus said. "I heard you running part of the way, too."

"Uh-huh," Rosie said, "Now tell me the secret."

"I was afraid you wouldn't come," he said.

Rosie delved around on the chicken-wire bottom of the stall for number two tomatoes, ripe, which she was sitting beside, and came up with a left-over that felt edible. She bit into it and began sucking out the pulp and seeds. "I'm here," she pointed out.

"Rosie, are you sorry you came?"

"Sorry? What for?" she said. "You said you were going to tell me something."

"I will, I will," Jesus said, but his voice contained disappointment, and Rosie, fleetingly, felt the older of the two, realizing a brand-new power which vanished without category under her recognition.

"I have to go back in a minute," she said. "My aunt and uncle are here from Wintersburg. I told them I was going to the privy."

Jesus laughed. "You funny thing," he said. "You slay me!"

"Just because you have a bathroom *inside*," Rosie said. "Come on, tell me."

Chuckling, Jesus came around to lean on the stand facing her. They still could not see each other very clearly, but Rosie noticed that Jesus became very sober again as he took the hollow tomato from her hand and dropped it back into the stall. When he took hold of her empty hand, she could find no words to protest; her vocabulary had become distressingly constricted and she thought desperately that all that remained intact now was yes and no and oh, and even these few sounds would not easily out. Thus, kissed by Jesus, Rosie fell, for the first time, entirely victim to a helplessness delectable beyond speech. But the terrible, beautiful sensation lasted no more than a second, and the reality of Jesus' lips and tongue and teeth and hands made her pull away with such strength that she nearly tumbled.

Rosie stopped running as she approached the lights from the windows of home. How long since she had left? She could not guess, but gasping yet, she went to the privy in back and locked herself in. Her own breathing deafened her in the dark, close space, and she sat and waited until she could hear at last the nightly calling of the frogs and crickets. Even then, all she could think to say was oh, my, and the pressure of Jesus' face against her face would not leave.

No one had missed her in the parlor, however, and Rosie walked in and through quickly, announcing that she was next going to take a bath. "Your father's in the bathhouse," her mother said, and Rosie, in her room, recalled that she had not seen him when she entered. There had been only Aunt Taka and Uncle Gimpachi with her mother at the table, drinking tea. She got her robe and straw sandals and crossed the parlor again to go outside. Her mother was telling them about the *haiku* competition in the *Mainichi* and the poem she had entered.

Rosie met her father coming out of the bathhouse. "Are you through, Father?" she asked. "I was going to ask you to scrub my back."

"Scrub your own back," he said shortly, going toward the main house.

"What have I done now?" she yelled after him. She suddenly felt like doing a lot of yelling. But he did not answer, and she went into the bathhouse. Turning on the dangling light, she removed her denims and T-shirt and threw them in the big carton for dirty clothes standing next to the washing machine. Her other things she took with her into the bath compartment to wash after her bath. After she had scooped a basin of hot water from the square wooden tub, she sat on the grey cement of the floor and soaped herself at exaggerated leisure, singing "Red Sails in the Sunset" at the top of her voice and using da-da-da where she suspected her words. Then, standing, still singing, for she was possessed by the notion that any attempt now to analyze would result in spoilage and she believed that the larger her volume the less she would be able to hear herself think, she obtained more hot water and poured it on until she was free of lather. Only then did she allow herself to step into the steaming vat, one leg first, then the remainder of her body inch by inch until the water no longer stung and she could move around at will.

She took a long time soaking, afterwards remembering to go around outside to stoke the embers of the tin-lined fireplace beneath the tub and to throw on a few more sticks so that the water might keep its heat for her mother, and when she finally returned to the parlor, she found her mother still talking *haiku* with her aunt and uncle, the three of them on another round of tea. Her father was nowhere in sight.

At Japanese school the next day (Wednesday, it was), Rosie was grave and giddy by turns. Preoccupied at her desk in the row for students on Book Eight, she made up for it at recess by performing wild mimicry for the benefit of her friend Chizuko. She held her nose and whined a witticism or two in what she considered was the manner of Fred Allen; she assumed intoxication and a British accent to go over the climax of the Rudy Vallee recording of the pub conversation about William Ewart Gladstone; she was the child Shirley Temple piping "On the Good Ship Lollipop"; she was the gentleman soprano of the Four Inkspots trilling "If I Didn't Care." And she felt reasonably satisfied when Chizuko wept and gasped, "Oh Rosie, you ought to be in the movies!"

Her father came after her at noon, bringing her sandwiches of minced ham and two nectarines to eat while she rode, so that she could pitch right into the sorting when they got home. The lugs were piling up, he said, and the ripe tomatoes in them would probably have to be taken to the cannery tomorrow if they were not ready for the produce haulers tonight. "This heat's not doing them any good. And we've got no time for a break today."

It *was* hot, probably the hottest day of the year, and Rosie's blouse stuck damply to her back even under the protection of the canvas. But she worked as efficiently as a flawless machine and kept the stalls heaped, with one part of her mind listening in to the parental murmuring about the heat and the tomatoes and with another part planning the exact words she would say to Jesus when he drove up with the first load of the afternoon. But when at last she saw that the pick-up was coming, her hands went berserk and the tomatoes started falling in the wrong stalls, and her father said, "Hey, hey! Rosie, watch what you're doing!"

"Well, I have to go to the *benjo*," she said, hiding panic.

"Go in the weeds over there," he said, only half-joking.

"Oh, Father!" she protested.

"Oh, go on home," her mother said. "We'll make out for awhile."

In the privy, Rosie peered through a knothole toward the fields, watching as much as she could of Jesus. Happily she thought she saw him look in the direction of the house from time to time before he finished unloading and went back toward the patch where his mother and father worked. As she was heading for the shed, a very presentable black car purred up the dirt driveway to the house and its driver motioned to her. Was this the Hayashi home, he wanted to know. She nodded. Was she a Hayashi? Yes, she said, thinking that he was good-looking man. He got out of the car with a huge, flat package and she saw that he warmly wore a business suit. "I have something here for your mother then," he said, in a more elegant Japanese than she was used to.

She told him where her mother was and he came along with her, patting his face with an immaculate white handkerchief and saying something about the coolness of San Francisco. To her surprised mother and father, he bowed and introduced himself as, among other things, the *haiku* editor of the *Mainichi Shimbun*, saying that since he had been coming as far as Los Angeles anyway, he had decided to bring her the first prize she had won in the recent contest.

"First prize?" her mother echoed, believing and not believing, pleased and overwhelmed. Handed the package with a bow, she bobbed her head up and down numerous times to express her utter gratitude.

"It is nothing much," he added, "but I hope it will serve as a token of our great appreciation for your contributions and our great admiration of your considerable talent."

"I am not worthy," she said, falling easily into his style. "It is I who should make some sign of my humble thanks for being permitted to contribute."

"No, no, to the contrary," he said, bowing again.

But Rosie's mother insisted, and then saying that she knew she was being unorthodox, she asked if she might open the package because her curiosity was so great. Certainly she might. In fact, he would like her reaction to it, for personally, it was one of his favorite *Hiroshiges*.

Rosie thought it was a pleasant picture, which looked to have been sketched with delicate quickness. There were pink clouds, containing some graceful calligraphy, and a sea that was a pale blue except at the edges, containing four sampans with indications of people in them. Pines edged the water and on the far-off beach there was a cluster of thatched huts towered over by pine-dotted mountains of grey and blue. The frame was scalloped and gilt.

After Rosie's mother pronounced it without peer and somewhat prodded her father into nodding agreement, she said Mr. Kuroda must at least have a cup of tea after coming all this way, and although Mr. Kuroda did not want to impose, he soon agreed that a cup of tea would be refreshing and went along with her to the house, carrying the picture for her.

"Ha, your mother's crazy!" Rosie's father said, and Rosie laughed uneasily as she resumed judgment on the tomatoes. She had emptied six lugs when he broke into an imaginary conversation with Jesus to tell her to go and remind her mother of the tomatoes, and she went slowly.

Mr. Kuroda was in his shirtsleeves expounding some *haiku* theory as he munched a rice cake, and her mother was rapt. Abashed in the great man's presence, Rosie stood next to her mother's chair until her mother looked up inquiringly, and then she started to whisper the message, but her mother pushed her gently away and reproached, "You are not being very polite to our guest."

"Father says the tomatoes..." Rosie said aloud, smiling foolishly.

"Tell him I shall only be a minute," her mother said, speaking the language of Mr. Kuroda.

When Rosie carried the reply to her father, he did not seem to hear and she said again, "Mother says she'll be back in a minute."

"All right, all right," he nodded, and they worked again in silence. But suddenly, her father uttered an incredible noise, exactly like the cork of a bottle popping, and the next Rosie knew, he was stalking angrily toward the house, almost running in fact, and she chased after him crying, "Father! Father! What are you going to do?"

He stopped long enough to order her back to the shed. "Never mind!" he shouted. "Get on with the sorting!"

And from the place in the fields where she stood, frightened and vacillating, Rosie saw her father enter the house. Soon Mr. Kuroda came out alone, putting on his coat. Mr. Kuroda got into his car and backed out down the driveway, onto the highway. Next her father emerged, also alone, something in his arms (it was the picture, she realized), and, going over to the bathhouse woodpile, he threw the picture on the ground and picked up the axe. Smashing the picture, glass and all (she heard the explosion faintly), he reached over for the kerosene that was used to encourage the bath fire and poured it over the wreckage. I am dreaming, Rosie said to herself, I am dreaming, but her father, having made sure that his act of cremation was irrevocable, was even then returning to the fields.

Rosie ran past him and toward the house. What had become of her mother? She burst into the parlor and found her mother at the back window, watching the dying fire. They watched together until there remained only a feeble smoke under the blazing sun. Her mother was very calm.

"Do you know why I married your father?" she said, without turning.

"No," said Rosie. It was the most frightening question she had ever been called upon to answer. Don't tell me now, she wanted to say, tell me tomorrow, tell me next week, don't tell me today. But she knew she would be told now, that the telling would combine with the other violence of the hot afternoon to level her life, her world to the very ground.

It was like a story out of the magazines illustrated in sepia, which she had consumed so greedily for a period until the information had somehow reached her that those wretchedly unhappy auto-biographies, offered to her as the testimonials of living men and women, were largely inventions: Her mother, at nineteen, had come to America and married her father as an alternative to suicide.

At eighteen, she had been in love with the first son of one of the well-to-do families in her village. The two had met whenever and wherever they could, secretly, because it would not have done for his family to see him favor her—her father had no money; he was a drunkard and a gambler besides. She had learned she was with child; an excellent match had already been arranged for her lover. Despised by her family, she had given premature birth to a stillborn son, who would be seventeen now. Her family did not turn her out, but she could no longer project herself in any direction without refreshing in them the memory of her indiscretion. She wrote to Aunt Taka, her favorite sister, in America, threatening to kill herself if Aunt Taka would not send for her. Aunt Taka hastily arranged a marriage with a young man of whom she knew, but lately arrived from Japan, a young man of simple mind, it was said, but of kindly heart. The young man was never told why his unseen betrothed was so eager to hasten the day of meeting.

The story was told perfectly, with neither groping for words nor untoward passion. It was as though her mother had memorized it by heart, reciting it to herself so many times over that its nagging vileness had long since gone.

"I had a brother then?" Rosie asked, for this was what seemed to matter now; she would think about the other later, she assured herself, pushing back the illumination which threatened all that darkness that had hitherto been merely mysterious or even glamorous. "A half-brother?"

"Yes."

"I would have liked a brother," she said.

Suddenly, her mother knelt on the floor and took her by the wrists. "Rosie," she said urgently. "Promise me you will never marry!" Shocked more by the request than the revelation, Rosie stared at her mother's face. Jesus, Jesus, she called silently, not certain whether she was invoking the help of the son of the Carrascos or of God, until there returned sweetly the memory of Jesus' hand, how it had touched her and where. Still her mother waited for an answer, holding her wrists so tightly that her hands were going numb. She tried to pull free. "Promise," her mother whispered fiercely, "promise." "Yes, yes, I promise," Rosie said. But for an instant she turned away, and her mother, hearing the familiar glib agreement, released her, Oh, you, you, you, her eyes and twisted mouth said, you fool. Rosie, covering her face, began at last to cry, and the embrace and consoling hand came much later than she expected.

Ten Years and More

～

BY

MIRIAM

WADDINGTON

When my husband
lay dying a mountain
a lake three
cities ten years
and more
lay between us:

There were our
sons my wounds
and theirs,
despair loneliness.
handfuls of un-
hammered nails
pictures never
hung all

The uneaten
meals and unslept
sleep; there was
retirement, and
worst of all
a green umbrella
he can never
take back.

I wrote him a
letter but all
I could think of
to say was: do you
remember Severn
River, the red canoe
with the sail
and lee-boards?

I was really saying
for the sake of our
youth and our love
I forgave him for
everything
and I was asking him
to forgive me too.

Maidens

~

BY

BONNIE

BISHOP

after seventy years of marriage
my grandma yelled
billy all i am is a nursemaid to you
go get it yourself

so grandpa did

and came out of the bathroom
with nailpolish on his nose
instead of mercurochrome

i am ashamed now
by my surprise
that she cried on
the day of his funeral

Here
In My Arms

~

BY

MARY

MELFI

It's better than holding a telephone
or a microphone in my hand,
much better than holding a pair of sunglasses
(or catching sunlight)
or holding a grocery bag in my arms.
It's even better than clutching
a purse stuffed with diamonds and pearls
because that's comfort
and comfort isn't more alive than I am—like sawdust.
This is alive. This is my baby and I need her to be
     here in my arms.

Mother and I, Walking

BY

LORNA

CROZIER

Father is gone again,
the streets empty.
Everyone is inside,
listening to radios
in the warm glow of their stoves.

The cold cries under our boots.
We wade through wind. It pushes
snow under my scarf and collar,
up the sleeves of my jacket.

Mother opens her old muskrat coat,
pulls me inside.
Her scent wraps around me.
The back of my head presses
into the warm rise of her belly.

When I lower my eyes, I see
our feet, mine between hers,
the tracks of one animal
crossing the open,
strange and nocturnal,
moving towards home.

My Oedipus Complex

BY

FRANK

O'CONNOR

ather was in the army all through the war—the first war, I mean—so, up to the age of five, I never saw much of him, and what I saw did not worry me. Sometimes I woke and there was a big figure in khaki peering down at me in the candlelight. Sometimes in the early morning I heard the slamming of the front door and the clatter of nailed boots down the cobbles of the lane. These were Father's entrances and exits. Like Santa Claus he came and went mysteriously.

In fact, I rather liked his visits, though it was an uncomfortable squeeze between Mother and him when I got into the big bed in the early morning. He smoked, which gave him a pleasant musty smell, and shaved, an operation of astounding interest. Each time he left a trail of souvenirs—model tanks and Gurkha knives with handles made of bullet cases, and German helmets and cap badges and button-sticks, and all sorts of military equipment—carefully stowed away in a long box on top of the wardrobe, in case they ever came in handy. There was a bit of the magpie about Father; he expected everything to come in handy. When his back was turned, Mother let me get a chair and rummage through his treasures. She didn't seem to think so highly of them as he did.

The war was the most peaceful period of my life. The window of my attic faced southeast. My mother had curtained it, but that had small effect. I always woke with the first light and, with all the responsibilities of the previous day melted, feeling myself rather like the sun, ready to illumine and rejoice. Life never seemed so simple and clear and full of possibilities as then. I put my feet out from under the clothes—I called them Mrs. Left and Mrs. Right—and invented dramatic situations for them in which they discussed the problems of the day. At least Mrs. Right did; she was very demonstrative, but I hadn't the same control of Mrs. Left, so she mostly contented herself with nodding agreement.

They discussed what Mother and I should do during the day, what Santa Claus should give a fellow for Christmas, and what steps should be taken to brighten the home. There was that little matter of the baby, for instance. Mother and I could never agree about that. Ours was the only house in the terrace without a new baby, and Mother said we couldn't afford one till Father came back from the war because they cost seventeen and six. That showed how simple she was. The Geneys up the road had a baby, and everyone knew they couldn't afford seventeen and six. It was probably a cheap baby, and Mother wanted something really good, but I felt she was too exclusive. The Geneys' baby would have done us fine.

Having settled my plans for the day, I got up, put a chair under the attic window, and lifted the frame high enough to stick out my head. The window overlooked the front gardens of the terrace behind ours, and beyond these it looked over a deep valley to the tall, red-brick houses terraced up the opposite hillside, which were all still in shadow, while those at our side of the valley were all lit up, though with long strange shadows that made them seem unfamiliar; rigid and painted.

After that I went into Mother's room and climbed into the big bed. She awoke and I began to tell her of my schemes. By this time, though I never seem to have noticed it, I was petrified in my nightshirt, and I thawed as I talked until, the last frost melted, I fell asleep beside her and woke again only when I heard her below in the kitchen, making the breakfast.

After breakfast we went into town; heard Mass at St. Augustine's and said a prayer for Father, and did the shopping. If the afternoon was fine we either went for a walk in the country or a visit to Mother's great friend in the convent, Mother St. Dominic. Mother had them all praying for Father, and every night, going to bed, I asked God to send him back safe from the war to us. Little, indeed, did I know what I was praying for!

One morning, I got into the big bed, and there, sure enough, was Father in his usual Santa Claus manner, but later, instead of his uniform, he put on his best blue suit, and Mother was as pleased as anything. I saw nothing to be pleased about, because, out of uniform, Father was altogether less interesting, but she only beamed, and explained that our prayers had been answered, and off we went to Mass to thank God for having brought Father safely home.

The irony of it! That very day when he came in to dinner he took off his boots and put on his slippers, donned the dirty old cap he wore about the house to save him from colds, crossed his legs, and began to talk gravely to Mother, who looked anxious. Naturally, I disliked her looking anxious, because it destroyed her good looks, so I interrupted him.

"Just a moment, Larry!" she said gently.

This was only what she said when we had boring visitors, so I attached no importance to it and went on talking.

"Do be quiet, Larry!" she said impatiently. "Don't you hear me talking to Daddy?"

This was the first time I had heard those ominous words, "talking to Daddy," and I couldn't help feeling that if this was how God answered prayers, he couldn't listen to them very attentively.

"Why are you talking to Daddy?" I asked with as great a show of indifference as I could muster.

"Because Daddy and I have business to discuss. Now, don't interrupt again!"

In the afternoon, at Mother's request, Father took me for a walk. This time we went into town instead of out in the country, and I thought at first, in my usual optimistic way, that it might be an improvement. It was nothing of the sort. Father and I had quite different notions of a walk in town. He had no proper interest in trams, ships, and horses, and the only thing that seemed to divert him was talking to fellows as old as himself. When I wanted to stop he simply went on, dragging me behind him by the hand; when he wanted to stop I had no alternative but to do the same. I noticed that it seemed to be a sign that he wanted to stop for a long time whenever he leaned against a wall. The second time I saw him do it I got wild. He seemed to be settling himself forever. I pulled him by the coat and trousers, but, unlike Mother who, if you were too persistent, got into a wax and said: "Larry, if you don't behave yourself, I'll give you a good slap," Father had an extraordinary capacity for amiable inattention. I sized him up and wondered would I cry, but he seemed to be too remote to be annoyed even by that. Really, it was like going for a walk with a mountain! He either ignored the wrenching and pummelling entirely, or else glanced down with a grin of amusement from his peak. I had never met anyone so absorbed in himself as he seemed.

At teatime, "talking to Daddy" began again, complicated this time by the fact that he had an evening paper, and every few minutes he put it down and told Mother something new out of it. I felt this was foul play. Man for man, I was prepared to compete with him any time for Mother's attention, but when he had it all made up for him by other people it left me no chance. Several times I tried to change the subject without success.

"You must be quiet while Daddy is reading, Larry," Mother said impatiently.

It was clear that she either genuinely liked talking to Father better than talking to me, or else that he had some terrible hold on her which made her afraid to admit the truth.

"Mummy," I said that night when she was tucking me up, "do you think if I prayed hard God would send Daddy back to the war?"

She seemed to think about that for a moment.

"No, dear," she said with a smile. "I don't think he would."

"Why wouldn't he, Mummy?"

"Because there isn't a war any longer, dear."

"But, Mummy, couldn't God make another war, if He liked?"

"He wouldn't like to dear. It's not God who makes wars, but bad people."

"Oh!" I said.

I was disappointed about that. I began to think that God wasn't quite what he was cracked up to be.

Next morning I woke at my usual hour, feeling like a bottle of champagne. I put out my feet and invented a long conversation in which Mrs. Right talked of the troubles she had with her own father till she put him in the Home. I didn't quite know what the Home was but it sounded the right place for Father. Then I got my chair and stuck my head out of the attic window. Dawn was just breaking, with a guilty air that made me feel I had caught it in the act. My head bursting with stories and schemes, I stumbled in next door, and in the half-darkness scrambled into the big bed. There was no room at Mother's side so I had to get between her and Father. For the time being I had forgotten about him, and for several minutes I sat bolt upright, racking my brains to know what I could do with him. He was taking up more than his fair share of the bed, and I couldn't get comfortable, so I gave him several kicks that made him grunt and stretch. He made room all right, though. Mother waked and felt for me. I settled back comfortably in the warmth of the bed with my thumb in my mouth.

"Mummy!" I hummed, loudly and contentedly.

"Sssh! dear," she whispered. "Don't wake Daddy!"

This was a new development, which threatened to be even more serious than "talking to Daddy." Life without my early-morning conferences was unthinkable.

"Why?" I asked severely.

"Because poor Daddy is tired."

This seemed to me a quite inadequate reason, and I was sickened by the sentimentality of her "poor Daddy." I never liked that sort of gush; it always struck me as insincere.

"Oh!" I said lightly. Then in my most winning tone: "Do you know where I want to go with you today, Mummy?"

"No, dear," she sighed.

"I want to go down the Glen and fish for thornybacks with my new net, and then I want to go out to the Fox and Hounds, and—"

"Don't-wake-Daddy!" she hissed angrily, clapping her hand across my mouth.

But it was too late. He was awake, or nearly so. He grunted and reached for the matches. Then he stared incredulously at his watch.

"Like a cup of tea, dear?" asked Mother in a meek, hushed voice I had never heard her use before. It sounded almost as though she were afraid.

"Tea?" he exclaimed indignantly. "Do you know what the time is?"

"And after that I want to go up the Rathcooney Road," I said loudly, afraid I'd forget something in all those interruptions.

"Go to sleep at once, Larry!" she said sharply.

I began to snivel. I couldn't concentrate, the way that pair went on, and smothering my early-morning schemes was like burying a family from the cradle.

Father said nothing, but lit his pipe and sucked it, looking out into the shadows without minding Mother or me. I knew he was mad. Every time I made a remark Mother hushed me irritably. I was mortified. I felt it wasn't fair; there was even something sinister in it. Every time I had pointed out to her the waste of making two beds when we could both sleep in one, she had told me it was healthier like that, and now here was this man, this stranger, sleeping with her without the least regard for her health!

He got up early and made tea, but though he brought Mother a cup he brought none for me.

"Mummy," I shouted, "I want a cup of tea, too."

"Yes, dear," she said patiently. "You can drink from Mummy's saucer."

That settled it. Either Father or I would have to leave the house. I didn't want to drink from Mother's saucer; I wanted to be treated as an equal in my own home, so, just to spite her, I drank it all and left none for her. She took that quietly, too.

But that night when she was putting me to bed she said gently:

"Larry, I want you to promise me something."

"What is it?" I asked.

"Not to come in and disturb poor Daddy in the morning. Promise?"

"Poor Daddy" again! I was becoming suspicious of everything involving that quite impossible man.

"Why?" I asked.

"Because poor Daddy is worried and tired and he doesn't sleep well."

"Why doesn't he, Mummy?"

"Well, you know, don't you, that while he was at the war Mummy got the pennies from the Post Office?"

"From Miss MacCarthy?"

"That's right. But now, you see, Miss MacCarthy hasn't any more pennies, so Daddy must go out and find us some. You know what would happen if he couldn't?"

"No," I said, "tell us."

"Well, I think we might have to go out and beg for them like the poor old woman on Fridays. We wouldn't like that, would we?"

"No," I agreed. "We wouldn't."

"So you'll promise not to come in and wake him?"

"Promise."

Mind you, I meant that. I knew pennies were a serious matter, and I was all against having to go out and beg like the old woman on Fridays. Mother laid out all my toys in a complete ring around the bed so that, whatever way I got out, I was bound to fall over one of them.

When I woke I remembered my promise all right. I got up and sat on the floor and played—for hours, it seemed to me. Then I got my chair and looked out the attic window for more hours. I wished it was time for Father to wake; I wished someone would make me a cup of tea. I didn't feel in the least like the sun; instead, I was bored and so very, very cold! I simply longed for the warmth and depth of the big featherbed.

At last I could stand it no longer. I went into the next room. As there was still no room at Mother's side I climbed over her and she woke with a start.

"Larry," she whispered, gripping my arm very tightly, "what did you promise?"

"But I did, Mummy," I wailed, caught in the very act. "I was quiet for ever so long."

"Oh, dear, and you're perished!" she said sadly, feeling me all over. "Now, if I let you stay will you promise not to talk?"

"But I want to talk, Mummy," I wailed.

"That has nothing to do with it," she said with a firmness that was new to me. "Daddy wants to sleep. Now, do you understand that?"

I understood it only too well. I wanted to talk, he wanted to sleep—whose house was it, anyway?

"Mummy," I said with equal firmness, "I think it would be healthier for Daddy to sleep in his own bed."

That seemed to stagger her, because she said nothing for a while.

"Now, once for all," she went on "you're to be perfectly quiet or go back to your own bed. Which is it to be?"

The injustice of it got me down. I had convicted her out of her own mouth of inconsistency and unreasonableness, and she hadn't even attempted to reply. Full of spite, I gave Father a kick, which she didn't notice but which made him grunt and open his eyes in alarm.

"What time is it?" he asked in a panic-stricken voice, not looking at Mother but at the door, as if he saw someone there.

"It's early yet," she replied soothingly. "It's only the child. Go to sleep again...Now, Larry," she added, getting out of bed, "you've wakened Daddy and you must go back."

This time, for all her quiet air, I knew she meant it, and knew that my principal rights and privileges were as good as lost unless I assessed them at once. As she lifted me, I gave a screech, enough to wake the dead, not to mind Father. He groaned.

"That damn child! Doesn't he ever sleep?"

"It's only a habit, dear," she said quietly, though I could see she was vexed.

"Well, it's time he got out of it," shouted Father, beginning to heave in the bed. He suddenly gathered all the bedclothes about him, turned to the wall, and then looked back over his shoulder with nothing showing only two small, spiteful, dark eyes. The man looked very wicked.

To open the bedroom door, Mother had to let me down, and I broke free and dashed for the farthest corner, screeching. Father sat bolt upright in bed.

"Shut up, you little puppy!" he said in a choking voice.

I was so astonished that I stopped screeching. Never, never had anyone spoken to me in that tone before. I looked at him incredulously and saw his face convulsed with rage. It was only then that I fully realized how God had codded me, listening to my prayers for the safe return of this monster.

"Shut up, you!" I bawled, beside myself.

"What's that you said?" shouted Father, making a wild leap out of bed.

"Mick, Mick!" cried Mother. "Don't you see the child isn't used to you?"

"I see he's better fed than taught," snarled Father, waving his arms wildly. "He wants his bottom smacked."

All his previous shouting was as nothing to these obscene words referring to my person. They really made my blood boil.

"Smack your own!" I screamed hysterically. "Smack your own! Shut up! Shut up!"

At this he lost his patience and let fly at me. He did it with the lack of conviction you'd expect of a man under Mother's horrified eyes, and it ended up as a mere tap, but the sheer indignity of being struck at all by a stranger, a total stranger who had cajoled his way back from the war into our big bed as a result of my innocent intercession, made me completely dotty. I shrieked and shrieked, and danced in my bare feet, and Father, looking awkward and hairy in nothing but a short gray army shirt, glared down at me like a mountain out for murder. I think it must have been then that I realized he was jealous too. And there stood Mother in her nightdress, looking as if her heart was broken between us. I hoped she felt as she looked. It seemed to me that she deserved it all.

From that morning out my life was a hell. Father and I were enemies, open and avowed. We conducted a series of skirmishes against one another, he trying to steal my time with Mother and I his. When she was sitting on my bed, telling me a story, he took to looking for some pair of old boots which he alleged he had left behind him at the beginning of the war. While he talked to Mother I played loudly with my toys to show my total lack of concern. He created a terrible scene one evening when he came in from work and found me at his box, playing with his regimental badges, Gurkha knives and button-sticks. Mother got up and took the box from me.

"You mustn't play with Daddy's toys unless he lets you, Larry," she said severely. "Daddy doesn't play with yours."

For some reason Father looked at her as if she had struck him and then turned away with a scowl.

"Those are not toys," he growled, taking down the box again to see had I lifted anything. "Some of those curios are very rare and valuable."

But as time went on I saw more and more how he managed to alienate Mother and me. What made it worse was that I couldn't grasp his method or see what attraction he had for Mother. In every possible way he was less winning than I. He had a common accent and made noises at his tea. I thought for a while that it might be the newspapers she was interested in, so I made up bits of news of my own to read to her. Then I thought it might be the smoking, which I personally thought attractive, and took his pipes and went round the house dribbling into them till he caught me. I even made noises at my tea, but Mother only told me I was disgusting. It all seemed to hinge round that unhealthy habit of sleeping together, so I made a point of dropping into their bedroom and nosing round, talking to myself, so that they wouldn't know I was watching them, but they were never up to anything that I could see. In the end it beat me. It seemed to depend on being grown-up and giving people rings, and I realized I'd have to wait.

But at the same time I wanted him to see that I was only waiting, not giving up the fight. One evening when he was being particularly obnoxious, chattering away well above my head, I let him have it.

"Mummy," I said, "do you know what I'm going to do when I grow up?"

"No, dear," she replied. "What?"

"I'm going to marry you," I said quietly.

Father gave a great guffaw out of him, but he didn't take me in. I knew it must only be pretense. And Mother, in spite of everything, was pleased. I felt she was probably relieved to know that one day Father's hold on her would be broken.

"Won't that be nice?" she said with a smile.

"It'll be very nice," I said confidently. "Because we're going to have lots and lots of babies."

"That's right, dear," she said placidly. "I think we'll have one soon, and then you'll have plenty of company."

I was no end pleased about that because it showed that in spite of the way she gave in to Father she still considered my wishes. Besides, it would put the Geneys in their place.

It didn't turn out like that, though. To begin with, she was very preoccupied—I supposed about where she would get the seventeen and six—and though Father took to staying out late in the evenings it did me no particular good. She stopped taking me for walks, became as touchy as blazes, and smacked me for nothing at all. Sometimes I wished I'd never mentioned the confounded baby—I seemed to have a genius for bringing calamity on myself.

And calamity it was! Sonny arrived in the most appalling hullabaloo—even that much he couldn't do without a fuss—and from the first moment I disliked him. He was a difficult child—so far as I was concerned he was always difficult—and demanded far too much attention. Mother was simply silly about him, and couldn't see when he was only showing off. As company he was worse than useless. He slept all day, and I had to go round the house on tiptoe to avoid waking him. It wasn't any longer a question of not waking Father. The slogan now was "Don't-wake-Sonny!" I couldn't understand why the child wouldn't sleep at the proper time, so whenever Mother's back was turned I woke him. Sometimes to keep him awake I pinched him as well. Mother caught me at it one day and gave me a most unmerciful flaking.

One evening, when Father was coming in from work, I was playing trains in the front garden. I let on not to notice him; instead, I pretended to be talking to myself, and said in a loud voice: "If another bloody baby comes into this house, I'm going out."

Father stopped dead and looked at me over his shoulder.

"What's that you said?" he asked sternly.

"I was only talking to myself," I replied, trying to conceal my panic. "It's private."

He turned and went in without a word. Mind you, I intended it as a solemn warning, but its effect was quite different. Father started being quite nice to me. I could understand that, of course, Mother was quite sickening about Sonny. Even at mealtimes she'd get up and gawk at him in the cradle with an idiotic smile, and tell Father to do the same. He was always polite about it, but he looked so puzzled you could see he didn't know what she was talking about. He complained of the way Sonny cried at night, but she only got cross and said that Sonny never cried except when there was something up with him—which was a flaming lie, because Sonny never had anything up with him and only cried for attention. It was really painful to see how simpleminded she was. Father wasn't attractive, but he had a fine intelligence. He saw through Sonny, and now he knew that I saw through him as well.

One night I woke with a start. There was someone beside me in the bed. For one wild moment I felt sure it must be Mother, having come to her senses and left Father for good, but then I heard Sonny in convulsions in the next room, and Mother saying: "There! There! There!" and I knew it wasn't she. It was Father. He was lying beside me, wide awake, breathing hard and apparently as mad as hell.

After a while it came to me what he was mad about. It was his turn now. After turning me out of the big bed, he had been turned out himself. Mother had no consideration now for anyone but that poisonous pup, Sonny. I couldn't help feeling sorry for Father. I had been through it all myself, and even at that age I was magnanimous. I began to stroke him down and say: "There! There!" He wasn't exactly responsive.

"Aren't you asleep either?" he snarled.

"Ah, come on and put your arm around us, can't you?" I said, and he did, in a sort of way. Gingerly, I suppose, is how you'd describe it. He was very bony but better than nothing.

At Christmas he went out of his way to buy me a really nice model railway.

How
We Kept
Mother's Day

BY

STEPHEN

LEACOCK

f all the different ideas that have been started lately, I think that the very best is the notion of celebrating once a year "Mother's Day." I don't wonder that May the eleventh is becoming such a popular date all over America and I am sure the idea will spread to England too.

It is especially in a big family like ours that such an idea takes hold. So we decided to have a special celebration of Mother's Day. We thought it a fine idea. It made us all realize how much Mother had done for us for years, and all the efforts and sacrifice that she had made for our sake.

So we decided that we'd make it a great day, a holiday for all the family, and do everything we could do to make Mother happy. Father decided to take a holiday from his office, so as to help in celebrating the day, and my sister Anne and I stayed home from college classes, and Mary and my brother Will stayed home from High School.

It was our plan to make it a day just like Xmas or any big holiday, and so we decided to decorate the house with flowers and with mottoes over the mantelpieces, and all that kind of thing. We got Mother to make mottoes and arrange the decorations, because she always does it at Xmas.

The two girls thought it would be a nice thing to dress in our very best for such a big occasion, and so they both got new hats. Mother trimmed both the hats, and they looked fine, and Father had bought four-in-hand silk ties for himself and us boys as a souvenir of the day to remember Mother by. We were going to get Mother a new hat too, but it turned out that she seemed to really like her old grey bonnet better than a new one, and both the girls said that it was awfully becoming to her.

Well, after breakfast we had it arranged as a surprise for Mother that we would hire a motor car and take her for a beautiful drive away into the country. Mother is hardly ever able to have a treat like that, because we can only afford to keep one maid, and so Mother is busy in the house nearly all the time. And of course the country is so lovely now that it would be just grand for her to have a lovely morning, driving for miles and miles.

But on the very morning of the day we changed the plan a little bit, because it occurred to Father that a thing it would be better to do even than to take Mother for a motor drive would be to take her fishing. Father said that as the car was hired and paid for, we might just as well use it for a drive up into the hills where the streams are. As Father said, if you just go out driving without any object, you have a sense of aimlessness, but if you are going to fish, there is a definite purpose in front of you to heighten the enjoyment.

So we all felt that it would be nicer for Mother to have a definite purpose; and anyway, it turned out that Father had just got a new rod the day before, which made the idea of fishing all the more appropriate, and he said that Mother could use it if she wanted to; in fact, he said it was practically for her, only Mother said she would much rather watch him fish and not try to fish herself.

So we got everything arranged for the trip, and we got Mother to cut up some sandwiches and make up a sort of lunch in case we got hungry, though of course we were to come back home again to a big dinner in the middle of the day, just like Xmas or New Year's Day. Mother packed it all up in a basket for us ready to go in the motor.

Well, when the car came to the door, it turned out that there hardly seemed as much room in it as we had supposed, because we hadn't reckoned on Father's fishing basket and the rods and the lunch, and it was plain enough that we couldn't all get in.

Father said not to mind him, he said that he could just as well stay home, and that he was sure that he could put in the time working in the garden; he said that there was a lot of rough dirty work that he could do, like digging a trench for the garbage, that would save hiring a man, and so he said that he'd stay home; he said that we were not to let the fact of his not having had a real holiday for three years stand in our way; he wanted us to go right ahead and be happy and have a big day, and not to mind him. He said that he could plug away all day, and in fact he said he'd been a fool to think there'd be any holiday for him.

But of course we all felt that it would never do to let Father stay home, especially as we knew he would make trouble if he did. The two girls, Anne and Mary, would gladly have stayed and helped the maid get dinner, only it seemed such a pity to, on a lovely day like this, having their new hats. But they both said that Mother had only to say the word, and they'd gladly stay home and work. Will and I would have dropped out, but unfortunately we wouldn't have been any use in getting the dinner.

So in the end it was decided that Mother would stay home and just have a lovely restful day around the house, and get the dinner. It turned out anyway that Mother doesn't care for fishing, and also it was just a little bit cold and fresh out of doors, though it was lovely and sunny, and Father was rather afraid that Mother might take cold if she came.

He said he would never forgive himself if he dragged Mother round the country and let her take a severe cold at a time when she might be having a beautiful rest. He said it was our duty to try and let Mother get all the rest and quiet that she could, after all that she had done for all of us, and he said that that was principally why he had fallen in with this idea of a fishing trip, so as to give Mother a little quiet. He said that young people seldom realize how much quiet means to people who are getting old. As to himself, he could still stand the racket, but he was glad to shelter Mother from it.

So we all drove away with three cheers for Mother, and Mother stood and watched us from the verandah for as long as she could see us, and Father waved his hand back to her every few minutes till he hit his hand on the back edge of the car, and then said that he didn't think Mother could see us any longer.

Well, we had the loveliest day up among the hills that you could possibly imagine, and Father caught such big specimens that he felt sure that Mother couldn't have landed them anyway, if she had been fishing for them, and Will and I fished too, though we didn't get so many as Father, and the two girls met quite a lot of people that they knew as we drove along, and there were some young men friends of theirs that they met along the stream and talked to, and so we all had a splendid time.

It was quite late when we got back, nearly seven o'clock in the evening, but Mother had guessed that we would be late, so she had kept back the dinner so as to have it just nicely ready and hot for us. Only first she had to get towels and soap for Father and clean things for him to put on, because he always gets so messed up with fishing, and that kept Mother busy for a little while, that and helping the girls get ready.

But at last everything was ready, and we sat down to the grandest kind of dinner—roast turkey and all sorts of things like on Xmas Day. Mother had to get up and down a good bit during the meal fetching things back and forward, but at the end Father noticed it and said she simply mustn't do it, that he wanted her to spare herself, and he got up and fetched the walnuts over from the sideboard himself.

The dinner lasted a long while, and was great fun, and when it was over all of us wanted to help clear the things up and wash the dishes, only Mother said that she would really much rather do it, and so we let her, because we wanted just for once to humour her.

It was quite late when it was all over, and when we all kissed Mother before going to bed, she said it had been the most wonderful day in her life, and I think there were tears in her eyes. So we all felt awfully repaid for all that we had done.

Johnnie's Poem

BY ALDEN NOWLAN

Look! I've written a poem!
Johnnie says
and hands it to me
            and it's about
            his grandfather dying
            last summer, and me
            in the hospital
and I want to cry,
don't you see, because it doesn't matter
if it's not very good:
            what matters is he knows
and it was me, his father, who told him
            you write poems about what
            you feel deepest and hardest.

Potato Planters

~

BY

LORNA

CROZIER

My father digs the hole
my mother drops the potato in—
she's cut them
so each piece has an eye

I wait till my father
empties his shovel
then stamp the earth
with my bare feet

Always it is May
it is after supper
when my father is home
still in his workboots
with the steel toes
his hands smelling
of machines and oil

Later there will be a moon
round and white
as the new potatoes
my mother boils
with milk and peas

I walk behind them
my feet loving the damp earth
my footprints all over the ground

Even now I see us
moving single file in the fading light
we three the last thing
the eye of the potato sees

from Jin Guo:

Voices of Chinese Canadian Women

Grace Lee

My mother didn't have to do anything except raise the children and be a missus! All the wives of the three nearby households led similar lives. They didn't play *mah jong* or gamble. They liked to wear beautiful clothes and dress up their children. They were very beautiful. My mother didn't even have to do any cooking in those days. All the meals were cooked and sent up by the people in our store. We were really very comfortable.

My father went back to China frequently and all my older brothers were already in Canada. The whole family returned to China when my father retired. I don't know how old he was at that time, but he was quite old. Men in those days all had several wives. My father had three wives. Only my mother didn't have bound feet. My father took a third wife because he consulted a geomancer who said that my mother wouldn't have a long life, so he had better bring in a third wife to look after him.... My mother lived to be ninety-six! You don't know the problems of large families, but my father was very loyal to all his wives and children, treating them all the same. However, I didn't like his authoritarianism. I wanted my freedom.

When I came back to China for a visit after teaching in Canada for a few years, my father was so happy and invited everyone to dinner. I told him that he didn't have to support me because I could earn my own money. So I started to communicate with him. Girls then did not talk to their fathers. I was twenty-nine years old when I went back to see my father after he had chased me away.

Towards the end of his life, my father said I was the best of all of his seventeen children. He finally knew me in the end. I looked after my mother afterwards and she came to live with me in Canada. She was seventy-five and I was forty-five.

Myrtle Wong

My mother stuck to Chinese tradition—she favoured the boys. This favouritism hurt deeply. Whenever we were involved in some physical fight, even though I was the wounded one, Mother used to ignore me and just rush to the aid of her son and sympathize with him. And I'd be left holding my open wound. Because we were taught filial piety, I didn't express my resentment to my parents...but I used to cry by myself.

Mother married Dad when she was fourteen. She had her first child at fifteen. She felt lonely in Australia because she couldn't speak English, so I used to take her out and act as her translator. No, we didn't get close. I just did these things for her because it was my duty. I helped her a lot with the housework. She was a fragile type of woman who needed support from someone.

My father was very old-fashioned. He would not let my mother have any say in matters concerning the family. He wanted to make all the decisions—even concerning what to serve dinner guests. He manipulated her like a puppet, giving her no freedom to think for herself.

Fern Hum

My mother always said that she wanted only one child (laugh). For the first seven years of her marriage, she was pregnant every year! Imagine five little kids who didn't go to school yet! I would have gone nuts! She delivered all of us at home, except for the first one. In those days there wasn't any medicare, so going to the hospital was expensive and my father couldn't afford it.

The Chinese women's group in Sudbury was my mother's only

social outlet. She didn't have much else. The group was formed by a few women in the church who wanted to reach out to the entire Chinese community through the Chinese women, since most of them were at home in those days. No, I don't think they were involved in cultural activities. It was more a social thing. There were probably some Bible lessons involved, I'm not really sure. But it was the church that most of the Chinese women went to. My mother was the first Chinese woman to come to Sudbury. Shortly after the Exclusion Act was lifted, other Chinese women began coming. But my mother felt quite isolated in the beginning....

My father had a daughter from a common-law marriage which my mother didn't even know about until she came over to Canada. She was very angry when she found out about it. She held bitterness about it until her death a couple of years ago. I think she felt cheated a lot. Many times she said if she had known about certain things before, she would not have married my father.

My parents married here in Canada. According to my mother, my father sent the fare over to China, so she could come to Canada, and she repaid him later on with money she earned from her own bean sprout business—yes, she had a small business by herself. At that time, Chinese food was becoming kind of popular. People were sort of accepting things like chop suey and egg rolls, the kind that you fry with the wonton skin. So she started this little business and managed to make a bit of money.

No, my father didn't see my mother before she came here. There were only pictures exchanged. My mother kept on saying (laugh), "He sent a younger picture." Also, my father was almost fifteen years older than my mother. All these things made my mother very bitter throughout the marriage. I guess my father's illegitimate daughter was topping on the cake. There were many complicated things in their marriage—and in our family life. But I think of my mother as a very brave person who didn't waver under these circumstances. She held her own...and was very loyal. I mean, nowadays, a lot of people, once they hear this, they'd ask for a divorce. I don't know if she *could* have left. I don't think she had enough money to get a fare back to China. I don't think she would have known who to contact to get a ticket for the ship. There weren't many travel agents who spoke Chinese. And how would she have been able to re-establish herself back in China—or even Hong Kong? No, she was more or less stuck in Canada.

She came into a very small mining community in which the majority of the people were English speaking. There were very few facilities where she could speak Chinese and get her points across. She had to stay where she was and deal with the situation and try to learn some English and maybe make some headway that way.

Later, as a teenager and into adulthood, I would hear more of the frustration she faced. She didn't say too much when I was younger, except that I knew she didn't like my half-sister. She wouldn't allow her to live with us, so my half-sister went from foster home to foster home—and, consequently, did not have a very stable family life. Occasionally, between foster homes, my father would bring my sister to our home, hoping that my mother would eventually accept his other daughter. But I don't think she ever did.

At first I was angry with my father for putting my mother in this situation. I also felt angry with my mother for rejecting her step-daughter. I thought that my mother should have been a bit more forgiving and allow my older sister to be part of our family even though she was not of the same mother.

When I got older, when I understood a bit more Chinese history, I was able to have some sympathy for my father. I know a couple of other Chinese families in Sudbury who have illegitimate children from the fathers' common-law relationships with white women, particularly French-Canadian women. Since most of these men didn't have Chinese spouses here in Canada, some of them took up common-law marriages because there was a need for some kind of loving relationship.

Jean Lee

My mother was old-fashioned. She thought that when we marry, we're no longer Hongs—so she gave everything to my brother. When my dad died he didn't have a will. At that time I signed over some papers to my mother so she could have the building and collect the rent for a lifetime. And she promised to give it back to us—because before Dad died, he said, "Boys are the same as girls. You must treat them the same because if it wasn't for the girls in this family, we would be broke and on welfare." We, the girls, were the ones who paid off the mortgage on the building! But my mother told us she changed her will: "Now, I'm going to leave two thirds to Sui because he's a Hong, to carry on the family name." So we figured one third between me and my sister, okay...but when she died a few years ago, we found out it was one third split between me and my sister *and* my brother's wife and three children! Ha! So that really left him with ninety percent and us with just five percent! My sister and I were very upset.

I guess my mother felt she had to look after her son. He was the only son left, since two other sons were killed in Europe during the war. Then the youngest one was killed in a motorcycle accident. So she sort of doted on her remaining son. His was an arranged marriage because he'd married a woman with a poor reputation and got divorced. Mother paid for his divorce and sent him to China and arranged for him to marry this second wife.... My sister and I are considering taking the case to court and having the will broken. That was...*really* a raw deal!

Victoria Yip

Most of the old-fashioned Chinese, they like boys better than girls, but my uncle and my father valued the girls far more than the boys. I know our family was unusual. I mean, for instance, every Sunday we used to hire a taxi to go to Beacon Hill Park or Mount Douglas Park to look at the view. None of the other Chinese families did that. My father knew all the plants and he'd show us. We went to the hills to pick green onions, wild green onions. Victoria is the only place I know that has them, and they're really delicious. We'd bring them home and make Chinese pancakes. You grated potato and put in pork and dried shrimp chopped up and the green onions. We would invite all our friends up, so we would be making it the whole day. I think my father did extra because my mother had died so young—when I was only eleven. My father was a very unusual man. We always went every Sunday to the cemetery which is near the sea. Then we would gather the shells, clams and seaweed and bring them all home.

Where Have All the Fathers Gone?

BY

REBECCA BAGGETT

~

My friend was stressed. She had to transport out-of-town guests to the airport, more than an hour's drive one way; her younger daughter was home with the flu; and her husband was to teach a class that met from two until four, the very same hours she would be en route to and from the airport. Could I, she asked, sit with Sarah while she was gone?

Reader, I said no. Softened with the suggestion that she call me back if she could find no one else. But no. And hung up the phone, shaking.

My friend is the last woman to give deliberate offense to anyone. Mild-tempered, organized in the extreme, an involved and loving mother, she works a demanding half-time job in the mornings and in the afternoons ferries her daughter to lessons. Her request was couched in the most tentative and apologetic terms; my no met with a rapid retreat, and I am certain she would be appalled if she knew that I spent the next quarter-hour pacing my office, in a towering rage.

What my friend was counting on was the support network, the half-mythical web of women that operated during our childhoods—the women who were "at home," available, and willing to pinch hit with a sick child, to pick up a few extra kids after school, to provide an afternoon's child care during school breaks so the "working mothers" could go to their offices. The network still exists, though its members are fewer than they were, but its assumptions have not changed one whit, and it is those assumptions that left me raging.

My friend knows something of the effort I have invested in my work, of the sacrifices of time and income I have made so that I will have time to write. And yet her request suggests that I am not practicing a profession but engaging in a hobby. Were she a single mother, I would have responded differently to her request—with equal reluctance, because I am trying never to yield on the question of whether my hours at home are work time, but for a friend who was a single mother, I would have packed a notebook and gone to sit with Sarah.

But Sarah has a father. A father whose work, it appears, is less easily interrupted than mine.

The network, you see, is also a support network for fathers. A network whose presumed smooth functioning permits them to avoid responsibility for their children. A network based on the assumption, which women's actions reaffirm, that interrupting men's work is not an acceptable solution to child care problems— which belong to mothers alone.

Don't get me wrong: I value our support networks. I have never believed that families function well in isolation. But I refuse to participate in a child-care network composed solely of mothers and existing for the privilege of fathers.

I remember times when my husband, a professor, and I have been faced with situations similar to the one Sarah's parents are facing today: Confronted with a sick child and my need to be elsewhere, my husband has canceled classes to stay home with our daughter. The university did not collapse, and his students did not suffer an irreparable gap in their educations. Everyone was inconvenienced, yes, but this is what happens when children are sick, and if fathers and their institutions have not yet learned to cope with that fact, it is high time they did.

The more things change, the more they stay the same. Nobody seems to be talking much these days about transforming the nuclear family, redefining roles, getting fathers involved with their children. We did all that in the 1970s, right? But Sarah is sick today, and it is unthinkable that her father interrupt his work to care for her, while both Sarah's parents think it not inappropriate to ask me to interrupt mine.

Although I feel guilty (of course, you nod), mostly, I am angry. With both of them, but particularly with my friend's husband, for whose sake I would be doing this favor, and who did not even have the courtesy to ask it of me himself. Who, it seems, regards this business of sick children as a matter for mothers, to be settled between us without subjecting him to the inconvenience of a phone call or the trouble of acknowledging that a favor has been asked.

I am angry for what this says about the relative worth of men's work and women's work, of work that earns money and work that rarely does, for what it says about the value of my work in my friend's eyes. And I am saddened by this confirmation that Sarah's father is not there for his daughters in ways I suspect he does not even imagine them to need him, by the realization that Sarah and her sister will no doubt grow up believing that the day-to-day needs of children are the concern of mothers alone, that they will probably expect and demand no more of their own children's fathers than their father gave to them. And so the cycle will continue, to everyone's loss—a cycle in which children's needs and women's work alike are devalued, while men's work is accorded an unreasonable and unjustified importance.

Househusbands

BY
RANDALL
BEACH

Don't you feel inadequate?"
"What about your career?"
"Can't you hack it in the workplace?"

In this ostensibly liberated age, these are the sorts of questions that "househusbands" frequently encounter when they explain that they, not their wives, are staying at home and raising the children. Contrary to what many people think, the househusband is still rare—and therefore isolated and misunderstood.

"It's still difficult for the man and for society," says Dr. Kyle Pruett, a clinical professor of psychiatry at the Yale School of Medicine's Child Study Center, who has done a five-year study of stay-at-home fathers. "Most men find themselves explaining what they're doing with the child at the supermarket week after week. The first response they get is, 'Isn't that lovely—you're babysitting!' But when it keeps happening, most men get pretty perturbed."

Harry Bishop, a 40-year-old stay-at-home father in Connecticut, made a crucial decision with his editor wife LuAnn, before his son, Cameron, now 19 months, was born. "We didn't like the idea of Cameron going right into day-care," he says. "And because of the high cost of day-care," he explains, "we knew we wouldn't lose that much money with one of us [quitting a job and] staying home. She had the better salary and a great health care plan."

And so Bishop, who was a newspaper staff photographer, quit his job. "I miss getting out, meeting people, and the work itself," he admits. "But I'm still doing photography, part time."

Although he doesn't regret his decision, Bishop says, "I have lost contact with a lot of my regular friends. I hardly see them anymore, unless I'm out working. That's probably been the biggest problem."

Yet as he danced around his backyard with Cameron on his shoulders, giggling, Bishop exulted over the rewards of his lifestyle: "It's fun. You get to act like a kid—one of the few times a grown man can get away with that. Any father would benefit from doing this, even for a week or two. You get an appreciation of what's involved in bringing a kid up. It's incredible how he's changed, how he's advancing."

Jerry Caporael-Katz is beginning to make the same discoveries about his kids. For many years he was executive director of an organization dealing with drug and alcohol abuse issues. But when his third child was born, he decided to cut back to part-time work and then eventually left his job altogether. Jerry's wife, Barbara Caporael-Katz, is a manager for a health maintenance organization.

"We used to both work 50 to 70 hours a week," he recalls. "I'd always feel guilty, coming home at 9 or 10 o'clock, when the kids were asleep. We asked ourselves, 'Is this worth it? Is this the best thing for the kids and us?' Then when Scotty was born, we decided we didn't want to live this way. I'm 44, somewhat a late-in-life father. To have someone else raise my kids just didn't make sense. We looked at both of our careers: Barbara has a better salary and benefits, less of a commute, and more work flexibility. We decided it made sense for me to stay at home."

He received some interesting reactions from his male friends: "Do you really know what you're doing?" and "Keep it quiet; if women hear about this, they'll want more of us to do it." His parents said, "You're doing *what*?" and then changed the subject. He says, "They think it's just a phase."

But Caporael-Katz is undaunted. "I'm seeing things through new perspectives, through my kids. Their imaginations are just exploding. It's so much fun, the spontaneous hugs and kisses. This is what I missed at work. I've read about 'quality time'; that's bogus. You can't just show up and say, 'O.K., I'm here to give you quality time.' They might be ready to take a nap."

Pruett says his study of stay-at-home fathers and their kids has shown that the dads developed an "anti-Rambo" attitude. "They were less defensively macho. Caring for another human being changes us all, men and women. It humanizes us.... The fathers become more considerate of their friends and families, find themselves more interested in human relationships, and are less competitive. But they don't lose their business sense or their edge. One father who kept at his real estate business said be became more efficient at negotiation because he learned to read people better."

Pruett says more fathers are becoming directly involved with child-rearing, even if they maintain their careers. "Men have a hunger for warm relationships. They've found that the BMW and condo are not what life is truly about. More men are asking for paternal leave and many companies now offer that. But it's not often used because men are still afraid it'll hurt their careers."

The best news from Pruett's study is this: The kids are all right. "They are doing well developmentally, better than normal in language, motor and social skills, problem-solving. This is very reassuring in those who worried whether men could raise children.... There is no gender confusion. The boys are comfortably masculine and the girls are comfortably feminine."

Pruett doesn't recommend that all families have full-time nurturing fathers, but he advises mothers, "Give your husband the opportunity to screw up a feeding; you'll find a partner who will get up in the middle of the night [to attend to a waiting infant]. Let him figure out how to bathe that baby."

However, Pruett doesn't see a complete social revolution happening; he believes that stay-at-home fathers will remain "an unusual phenomenon." David Royce of Westport, Connecticut, who stayed home to raise three kids (now aged 13, 11, and 6) thinks there are fewer men doing this today than there were 10 years ago. "I sometimes think the '60s are over," Royce says. "Househusbands like me are a dying breed. People are getting back into the old rut. With unequal pay scales for men and women, it's tempting for the men to knock off this 'househusband crap' and make a lot more money."

Station

BY
EAMON
GRENNAN

We are saying goodbye
on the platform. In silence
the huge train waits, crowding the station
with aftermath and longing
and all we've never said
to one another. He
shoulders his black bag and shifts
from foot to foot, restless to be off, his eyes
wandering over tinted windows where he'll sit
staring out at the Hudson's platinum dazzle.

I want to tell him he's entering into the light
of the world, but it feels like a long tunnel
as he leaves one home, one parent
for another,
and we both know it won't ever
be the same again. What is the air at,
heaping between us, then thinning
to nothing? Or those slategrey birds that ·
croon to themselves in an iron angle, then
take flight, inscribing
huge loops of effortless grace
between this station of shade and the shining water?

When our cheeks rest glancing against each other,
I can feel mine scratchy with beard and stubble, his
not quite smooth as a girl's, harder, a faint fuzz
starting—those silken beginnings I can see
when the light is right, his next life
in bright first touches. What ails our heart? Mine
aching in vain for the words
to make sense of our life together, his
fluttering in dread
of my finding the words, feathered syllables
fidgeting in his throat.

In a sudden rush of bodies
and announcements out of the air, he says
he's got to be going. One quick touch
and he's gone. In a minute
the train—ghostly faces behind smoked glass—
groans away on wheels and shackles, a slow glide
I walk beside, waving
at what I can see no longer. Later,
on his own in the city, he'll enter the underground
and cross the river, going home
to his mother's house: I imagine that white face
carried along in the dark glass, shining
through shadows that fill the window
and fall away again
before we're even able to name them.

"I Want to Go Home!"

BY

CLARA

LOVATT

I would have loved to have had Franny* for a grandmother or maybe an aunt. She's the kind of woman I picture myself being when I am 86. Along my journeys of seeking out alternative or more health-creating lifestyles, Franny may have been a mentor for me or a model of the strong woman if she had been my relative or neighbour.

Franny has dozed off to sleep in her wheelchair, leaving me sitting on the bedside near her, waiting a few moments, knowing that she will waken soon. She has been a resident at Cancare Nursing Home since 1988. When she was discharged from the chronic care ward of the local hospital, Franny's only living relative, her cousin, admitted her to Cancare. I am a 'visitor' and Franny was assigned to me by the Visiting Committee of my church. Apparently, when Joanna, Franny's cousin, admitted her, she told the Cancare staff that Franny was sometimes 'difficult', so when the Visiting Committee sought names of people at Cancare to visit, Franny's name was on the list.

* The names of the people and the places in this account of an elderly woman's experience have been changed.

I have heard Franny's stories many times. Now each time I listen, I hope I will be able to tempt Franny with a bit of her own history. I love encouraging her to add more detail or weave another thread through the tapestry of dreams and challenges that constitute her experience as a woman. I look at her now with her head gently resting forward in sleep and I see a firm profile and confident posture. The will of this woman has not been broken by her disabilities but I fear for the survival of her spirit.

Today, like she does most days, Franny told me that she wanted to go home. But today she was particularly insistent and more angry than usual about the fact that the Cancare staff is not letting her go. I know about Franny's home. It would be called a "Century Home" on today's real estate market. It is a comfortable looking yet impressive two storey red brick house on a corner lot of the main street in a small Ontario town. Across the street is the town park, heavily shaded by large oak trees where in the centre stands an old-time bandshell. Two blocks into town is the post office. Franny could describe her home and neighbourhood so well that when I eventually saw pictures, it all looked very familiar to me. Franny's mind often seems to live in this home that is now lost to her, while somehow her body functions here at Cancare. Franny presents a curious case for health caregivers. The term 'dementia' is sometimes used loosely to describe Franny's uncooperative behaviour, but 'difficult' is used more frequently.

This morning I met Franny in the hall, where she was wheeling herself back to her room after breakfast. Recognizing me, she grinned.

"Oh, it's you!" she exclaimed. "Have you come back to listen to an old woman complain?"

"Don't be silly Franny," I said. "I look forward to my visits with you. How was your time in the dining room this morning?"

Franny shrugged. "I get on with one or two at my table. I would rather be at home. Mr. Dickens handles my affairs. Would you tell him that I want the key to my house? I have to go home."

"But Franny," I offered lamely, "you already have a key to your house."

Who was I kidding? Certainly not Franny! Yes, she does indeed have a key to her house, but she knows she can't go home and she knows that I know it. We're told that the reason she can't leave is because she can't walk and therefore can't look after herself. It's apparently as simple as that! Franny says she feels like a prisoner here.

Franny was the eldest of two daughters. As a girl she was very close to her mother and sister, taking considerable family responsibility at a young age after her father died. Franny graduated from high school with the highest marks in the province and began a career as a legal secretary for a law firm in her home town. Over the course of her career, Franny acquired real estate and significant savings. She speaks often of two especially close friends who lived nearby her childhood home in which she lived all of her life until she was 83 years old. In this house Franny cared for her mother into her old age. After her mother's death, Franny continued living in this house for 37 years and her women friends were her community and support network.

Then Franny's life seemed to turn against her. It happened so unexpectedly on her way home from the post office. She had slipped on a hidden patch of ice and had broken her hip. Franny was taken to the hospital in an ambulance. Because there was no one living in her house to care for her after the surgery, Franny was then placed in the chronic care ward for an extended recovery period. She never did regain the use of her legs. During this hospitalization, it was the emotional and mental stress Franny felt that prompted her to give power of attorney with respect to the major decisions concerning her life and finances to Joanna. Moved either by compassion or frustration, Joanna signed Franny out of the hospital and into Cancare. These days Franny usually does not remember that she gave this power of attorney to Joanna, but when she does remember, she wants to take it away from her. It is felt at Cancare, when Franny gets angry, that she behaves selfishly and is unappreciative of Joanna's taking care of her business.

I happen to know that Franny wants a different person holding power of attorney because she has told me more than once. But she also tells me that she wants to go home because her mother needs her and that she wants Mr. Dickens to handle her affairs. Mr. Dickens is the name of the man she worked for when she was a young woman beginning her career. He has long since died.

I did an investigation once. Franny has enough money and investments to provide her with full-time nursing care in her own home for as long as she could possibly need it. The sums she tells me that she has, match up with her actual financial statements. I didn't have to do a lot of digging to find this information, but in the process I did get warned not to be "taken in" by Franny. I was then shown Franny's medical chart where it is written that Franny is manipulative and self-centred. It is also noted prior to this entry that Franny has "never married".

Naively wondering how Franny's never having been married had anything to do with her needs today, I scanned the chart looking for clues. It turns out that "never married" means that there is nothing to write on the form where the question about next of kin is asked. No further information is sought for the records about the woman's support community. The names of Franny's women friends, past and present, are absent.

The impact of the sexism overwhelmed me and I ended my investigation. I wasn't ready to face the harsh reality of my own old age. Franny could be me. This woman whom I admire for the strength and courage with which she lived, is today powerless and trapped by waves of sexism and heterosexism. Franny is thousands of women in Ontario today. But I must face my own fear of Franny's fate or I'll find myself scorning her protests and trivializing them by joining the voices of denial that define her experience of social injustice in terms of 'difficult' behaviour.

Franny is not adjusting well to Cancare life. Of course, I see that many women are fine here, especially when they have chosen to be here. But Franny says that her choice is to be at home where she should be, with her friends and taking care of her mother. Are her memories of community and feelings of being loved her crime or her dementia? Interpreted either way, it translates as 'difficult' to those wanting her to adapt to a place where she does not want to be.

Franny stirred.

"You're still here?" she queried, sitting up, her shoulders straightening.

I smiled. "Yes, Franny, I'm still here." I leaned closer and took her hands in mine.

"Good!" she said matter of factly. "I want you to read something for me."

Franny reached beside her for her purse and opened it. She carefully folded back a torn piece of the inside silk lining. My curiosity was piqued as I watched the certainty of her fingers. She finally pulled out a yellowed business card and handed it to me.

"What does this say?" she asked me.

The letterhead was the name of a funeral parlour. On the card was printed the name of Franny's mother and the date of her mother's death.

"Why Franny," I said in amazement. "This card says that your mother died exactly forty years ago today!"

"Yes," Franny said quietly. "I want to go home."

Brothers

BY

KATE

BRAID

We have worked together
eight hours every day,
five days every week,
four weeks every month,
for three months now.
Closer than a marriage almost
in the intensity of our days,
the joy in our joint production.

We have fought for each other
and refused to be separated
by other carpenters
or a foreman's whim
and yesterday they said
there will be layoffs next week.

Don't get excited, you said
when the tears sprang to my eyes.

Don't get excited, you have said before.
It is our joke of the past three months
and now I understand
that *excited* means *emotional.*
I'm not allowed to care on this job
yet you love me because I speak the unspoken.
I cry the tears for us all.

First Day on a New Jobsite

BY SUSAN EISENBERG

Never again a first day like the
First Day
            that Very First one,
when only the sternest vigilance
kept the right foot following the left
following the right following the left,
each step a decision, a victory of
willpower over fear, future over past.
Margaret's out there/Keep going/
She's been working a few
weeks already/She's managing/
*Keep going/*The legs buck
LA/Seattle/Detroit/women passing
through construction site gates for the
*first time/Keep going/*Right following
Go home if you want!/But
tomorrow/What'll you do for work
*tomorrow?/*left following right up to
the gate
            where a man hands me hardhat and
goggles and points me toward a trailer
where the conversation
                              stops
                              as I enter:
Well, what'll we talk about now.
Can't talk about girls.

And then Ronnie, the one with beady eyes
and a gimp leg, who knows for a fact—
        one of the girl apprentices
        is a stripper in the Zone—
says to my partner
                Give me your apprentice
and I follow him, tripping over cinderblocks,
to a small room
            where he points to the ceiling:
I need some hangers 11 inches off the ceiling/
Here's the Hilti/
The rod and strut are in the corner/
The ceiling's marked where I want
holes drilled and leaves
                without
          explaining
              hanger
              rod
              strut
or seeing that the bit on the heavy drill
barely reaches
           the x-marks on the ceiling
when I stand tiptoe on the ladder's
                top step.

Knowing which words to use
    what jokes to banter
    how to glide the body through dangers
        without knocking anything
           or anyone;
learning to speak first
    and define the territory
        of conversation
Passing.

* * *

Another
    first day: the job new
the workers all strangers, all men
myself   the only 'female'
        and yet
we find, almost easily, the language
that is common:
    —Get me some 4-inch squares
        with three-quarter k-o's—
    —Need any couplings or connectors?
    —No, but grab some clips and c-clamps
        and some half-inch quarter-twenties.
Passwords.
    —You know what you're doing in a panel?
    —Sure.

Mechanic to mechanic.
Never again a first day like the
First Day.

Simmering

~

BY

MARGARET

ATWOOD

t started in the backyards. At first the men concentrated on heat and smoke, and on dangerous thrusts with long forks. Their wives gave them aprons in railroad stripes, with slogans on the front—*Hot Stuff, The Boss*—to spur them on. Then it began to get all mixed up with who should do the dishes, and you can't fall back on paper plates forever, and around that time the wives got tired of making butterscotch brownies and jello salads with grated carrots and baby marshmallows in them and wanted to make money instead, and one thing led to another. The wives said that there were only twenty-four hours in a day; and the men, who in that century were still priding themselves on their rationality, had to agree that this was so.

For a while they worked it out that the men were in charge of the more masculine kinds of food: roasts, chops, steaks, dead chickens and ducks, gizzards, hearts, anything that had obviously been killed, that had visibly bled. The wives did the other things, the glazed parsnips and the prune whip, anything that flowered or fruited or was soft and gooey in the middle. That was all right for about a decade. Everyone praised the men to keep them going, and the wives, sneaking out of the houses in the mornings with their squeaky new briefcases, clutching their bus tickets because the men needed the station wagons to bring home the carcasses, felt they had got away with something.

But time is not static, and the men refused to stay put. They could not be kept isolated in their individual kitchens, kitchens into which the wives were allowed less and less frequently because, the men said, they did not sharpen the knives properly, if at all. The men began to acquire kitchen machines, which they would spend the weekends taking apart and oiling. There were a few accidents at first, a few lost fingers and ends of noses, but the men soon got the hang of it and branched out into other areas: automatic nutmeg graters, electric gadgets for taking the lids off jars. At cocktail parties they would gather in groups at one end of the room, exchanging private recipes and cooking yarns, tales of soufflés daringly saved at the last minute, pears flambées which had gone out of control and had to be fought to a standstill. Some of these stories had risqué phrases in them, such as *chicken breasts*. Indeed, sexual metaphor was changing: bowls and forks became prominent, and *eggbeater, pressure cooker* and *turkey baster* became words which only the most daring young women, the kind who thought it was a kick to butter their own toast, would venture to pronounce in mixed company. Men who could not cook very well hung about the edges of these groups, afraid to say much, admiring the older and more experienced ones, wishing they could be like them.

Soon after that, the men resigned from their jobs in large numbers so they could spend more time in the kitchen. The magazines said it was a modern trend. The wives were all driven off to work, whether they wanted to or not: someone had to make the money, and of course they did not want their husbands' masculinity to be threatened. A man's status in the community was now displayed by the length of his carving knives, by how many of them he had and how sharp he kept them, and by whether they were plain or ornamented with gold and precious jewels.

Exclusive clubs and secret societies sprang up. Men meeting for the first time would now exchange special handshakes—the Béchamel twist, the chocolate mousse double grip—to show that they had been initiated. It was pointed out to the women, who by this time did not go into the kitchens at all on pain of being thought unfeminine, that *chef* after all means *chief* and that Mixmasters were common but no one had ever heard of a Mixmistress. Psychological articles began to appear in magazines on the origin of women's kitchen envy and how it could be cured. Amputation of the tip of the tongue was recommended, and, as you know, became a wide-spread practice in the more advanced nations. If Nature had meant women to cook, it was said, God would have made carving knives round and with holes in them.

This is history. But it is not a history familiar to many people. It exists only in the few archival collections that have not yet been destroyed, and in manuscripts like this one, passed from woman to woman, usually at night, copied out by hand or memorized. It is subversive of me even to write these words. I am doing so, at the risk of my own personal freedom, because now, after so many centuries of stagnation, there are signs that hope and therefore change have once more become possible.

The women in their pinstripe suits, exiled to the livingrooms where they dutifully sip the glasses of port brought out to them by the men, used to sit uneasily, silently, listening to the loud bursts of male and somehow derisive laughter from behind the closed kitchen doors. But they have begun whispering to each other. When they are with those they trust, they tell of a time long ago, lost in the fogs of legend, hinted at in packets of letters found in attic trunks and in the cryptic frescoes on abandoned temple walls, when women too were allowed to participate in the ritual which now embodies the deepest religious convictions of our society: the transformation of the consecrated flour into the holy bread. At night they dream, long clandestine dreams, confused and obscured by shadows. They dream of plunging their hands into the earth, which is red as blood and soft, which is milky and warm. They dream that the earth gathers itself under their hands, swells, changes its form, flowers into a thousand shapes, for them too, for them once more. They dream of apples; they dream of the creation of the world; they dream of freedom.

Who Teaches Primary?

~

BY

CYNTHIA PRATT NICOLSON

oom nine at Waverly school in Vancouver buzzes with the voices of 23 lively six- and seven-year-olds. When these children finish printing stories in their personal journals, they'll move into class 'centres'—blocks, art, house corner, math games, and so on. The scene resembles primary classrooms across the country, with one major difference. Unlike the vast majority of young Canadian children, the kids in room nine are taught by a man.

Their teacher, Sol Pavony, began his career with young children in a daycare centre during the '70s. Since then, he's tutored children with special problems, worked as a faculty associate at Simon Fraser University and run an independent school. Now employed by the Vancouver School District, Pavony has taught various levels from kindergarten to grade three. What's it like to be one of the few men teaching in the early grades?

"I haven't felt any real barriers," Pavony says. "Some people think there's more status in teaching older kids but I think that's plain stupid. With young kids you have a greater influence—one year is 20 percent of a five-year-old's life!"

Though Pavony isn't alone, his male colleagues are few and far between. "Once I contacted another male kindergarten teacher in Prince George," says the tall, bearded teacher. "We discussed education philosophy by electronic mail. There are other men out there who teach kindergarten, but I don't know any personally."

Though real barriers may not be a problem, Pavony has experienced a definite lack of understanding within the school system. "When I was tutoring, I was automatically given high school students to work with," he says. "And one time when I was substitute teaching, I had a strange experience. They kept asking me if I really wanted to go to this one particular kindergarten class. I said okay, but they kept asking if I was sure. I had a fine morning with them and afterwards asked, 'What was the matter with that class?' 'Oh,' they said, 'we just thought you wouldn't want to teach them because you're a man.'"

[In 1991] men made up only 17 percent of the teaching staff in BC elementary schools. In Ontario, they held 28 percent of the full-time elementary teaching positions. Because most male elementary teachers work with older kids (grades four and up), these available statistics, while low, don't give a true picture of the drastic lack of men in the earliest grades. Across the country, children can easily go through several years of school without encountering a male teacher.

In this era of dads who diaper babies and tuck toddlers into bed, why are so few men teaching young kids? What happens when boys have no male role models for this important work?

"There's a whole constellation of issues that discourage young men from entering primary education," says Michael Fullan, dean of the Faculty of Education at the University of Toronto. "Built-in expectations make it awkward for a young man to say 'I think I want to teach young children'—it's like the situation with male nurses."

Fullan points out that "the idea permeates society that women are the caregivers." He continues, "Principals often don't think of men as primary teachers. Men are not seen as pursuing a successful career if they teach young children."

Glen Dixon, director of the Child Study Centre at UBC, agrees. He says, "There's a feeling that teaching five-year-olds all your life is not enough of a career for a man. That's regrettable." Dixon explains that men involved in early childhood and primary education usually move quickly into administrative or academic positions. "I've noticed a kind of expectation that often urges men into supervisory roles."

"There's also a tremendous concern with child abuse," adds this veteran of 30 years in early childhood education. "I've had to change. I may shake a child's hand or give a slight pat on the shoulder, but I keep my distance the whole time. I think it has a deterrent effect on some men—

they choose to teach children in higher grades."

In spite of these roadblocks, more men appear to be steering in the direction of early childhood and primary education. The University of Toronto has adopted the policy of encouraging men to enter elementary teaching. "Five years ago the problem existed but nobody talked about it," says Fullan. "Now the shortage of men teaching young children has been made explicit."

A brochure published by the university encourages men to "explore, discover and be challenged by a career in elementary school teaching." It comments, "It seems particularly disturbing that even today young boys from single-parent, mother-led families might not meet their first same-sex teacher until they arrive in high school. The absence of male role models at the elementary school level adversely affects the provision of quality education."

[Between 1990 and 1992], the university has raised the numbers of males in its elementary teacher certification program from ten to 22 percent. Fullan feels that the presence of these men in the teaching workforce will encourage other men to consider primary and early childhood education as a career.

Says Fullan, "The general discussion in our society of the need for men to be more open and caring in some ways makes it much more likely now for men to work with young children. What we would like to see is men seeing themselves as being able to establish personal rapport, to connect with the whole child, not only in the early years but throughout schooling."

Gender equity needs to work both ways. To the perennial adult question *What do you want to be when you grow up?*, we now encourage girls to answer 'an engineer' or 'a firefighter.' Let's not forget to tell boys that they can take on the worthwhile and exciting goal of becoming a 'kindergarten teacher.'

Invisible Women, Crossing Borders

~

BY

JEAN

MOLESKY-POZ

That Saturday morning was a moment when I came to realize how my personal life has become interwoven with "the invisible women" of California. Our little family of four was out strolling. Joseph, almost eight months, snuggled close to my breast. Joanna walked hand in hand with Martin. We stopped to watch a Japanese woman wrap sushi at a food cart on Fourth Street in Berkeley when an old Chevy pulled up to the curb. The driver jumped out of the car and in broken English asked for help. He unfolded a crumpled scrap of paper with the name and address of Tiny Tots Diaper Service. "*Sabes donde es*?" I glanced at the fifty-ish Mexican woman sitting in the passenger seat, her eyes downcast, her black hair pulled back. She took a quick look at Joseph and me. "My God!" I thought, "Joseph's diaper service—she's to wash dirty cotton diapers for a living!"

I saw Mexican women opening large plastic sacks, pulling tons of peed-in, shit-in diapers, the ammonia smells confined, condensed, and finally escaping into their faces. In other homes, other moms had tossed the diapers, let them sit in urine for seven days until the weekly pickup. A bag of thirty-six sterilized white cotton diapers wrapped in plastic would be delivered on our front porches Monday morning.

I had been teaching a course on immigrant women at the University of California, Berkeley, but it was that incident that "deterritorialized" me. That is, l lost my own sense of "home," lost my innocence. I knew, of course, that California's position on the Pacific Rim attracts newcomers across water and land borders. Twenty-five percent of our population is born outside the U.S. Fifty percent of the newcomers are women. Almost every aspect of our lives is touched by their lives. But now in almost every ritual of my day, I know how their hidden lives are part of my life.

As I slip on my clothing in the morning, I notice those labels in tiny print: "Made in Taiwan," "Made in Korea," "Made in Mexico." My shoes are stamped "Made in China." I've seen those sweatshops and know that many women have left rural areas to work in those urban garment factories lining the Pacific Rim. But it's happening here, too. The San Francisco Bay Area garment industry is now the third largest in the country. Most of the 12,000 workers are women who come from China, Hong Kong, and Taiwan. I heard Doris, a young woman who arrived from China in 1990, say:

> I thought there would be a lot of opportunities for my husband and me in the United States, but when we came to Oakland last year, we were very disappointed. I didn't have any skills, and I didn't know any English. The best job I could get was working in a garment shop that paid $1.50 an hour.

I help the children get dressed in the morning. Their clothing bears the same Pacific Rim labels. I toss plastic dinosaurs, farm animals, cars, trucks, Barbies, and the stuffed animals strewn on their beds back into the toy chest. The small of Barbie's back is stamped "Made in China," and the dinosaur's belly is imprinted "Made in Taiwan." Tags dangling off the teddy bears read "Made in Korea." I wonder under what working conditions and for what wages women have assembled these toys. At what expense to their personal lives?

In my morning seminar on immigrant women, students gather in the circle of chairs. Students from Ethiopia, Peru, China, Korea, Japan, Mexico, El Salvador, and the Philippines, along with others, generations removed from their African and European origins, await today's discussion on women from the North Pacific Rim.

"Women from Mexico play a new role in the global marketplace," I begin. I tell them that Mexican migration to California is marked by its circular pattern. Initially, in the mid-1870s, women were left behind in Mexico as their spouses, fathers, and sons were contracted by U.S. railroads, mines, and agricultural industries, and the women awaited their seasonal return. Later, women joined their families who had migrated and settled in California through the Bracero Program. I emphasize that Mexican migration today is marked by the new woman immigrant who initiates migration—the single woman, the single mother, the mother seeking employment opportunities and educational possibilities to support herself, her children, and often her parents, sisters, and brothers.

I want them to know the structural adversities these women encounter and explain that women migrating north take great risks in crossing the border, that they are vulnerable to physical assaults and rape by border patrolmen and border delinquents. Upon arrival, due to their undocumented status, limited proficiency in English, and non-transferable skills, they are restricted to entry-level jobs as seamstresses, assemblers, or farm laborers in garment, electronic, or agricultural industries. I want my students to understand why others find their choice of employment limited to the service sector as hotel- and housemaids, janitors, domestic workers, childcare workers, or caregivers to the elderly and sick. I hope they see how these women's undocumented status makes them more vulnerable to economic and sexual harassment and exploitation.

Myrna, a forty-year-old woman from El Salvador, explains that a friend of hers from Mexico was a single mother who sought work as a caregiver for the elderly:

> She wanted a live-in job to cover her room and board. She got hired to work six hours a day, but she works twenty-four hours a day. They pay her $4.20 per hour for the six hours of caregiving, but she also cooks, cleans, and does the laundry.

Maria de Jesus, twenty-eight, says:

> I could not deny him pleasure...because of what he paid for me. A couple of fellows held me down by the legs and forced me to have love that way...He said I had to do what he said because he paid for me, and I had no place else to go. The

world was closed off to me...Never, never would I have imagined all the horrible things that would happen to me in this country. I believe there would be a good, good fortune. People say we are lucky to be in this country. But we come here and hit a very cold reality. It's the same life or worse than what we had in the Third World.

"Asian immigrant women's stories, too, have been unheard until recently," I say, shifting our focus to Pacific migration. I explain how the lives of Asian immigrant women are structured into California's economy differently than were the lives of Chinese, Korean, and Japanese women 130 years ago. During the Gold Rush Era, prostitutes were almost always imported as indentured servants or *mui jai*, sold by poor parents in China, then resold for a gain in America. In fact, 85 percent of the Chinese women in mid-nineteenth-century San Francisco were brought over as prostitutes. There were similar patterns for early Japanese and Korean immigrant women. Between 1948 and 1953, 90 percent of immigrants from China, Japan, and Korea were women who joined husbands under the War Brides Act of 1946. Finally, I show that since the passage of the 1965 Immigration Law and the 1980 Refugee Act, more than half of the Asian immigrants are women. The factors that encourage them to migrate, and the contexts of their entry and resettlement, are very diverse.

Julie, a young woman of twenty-one, begins:

My parents believed so deeply in this version of the American dream that they were willing to sacrifice their solidarity as an arrangement in which my father stayed in Taiwan, earning a living, and occasionally visiting his family. My Mom said it was the only way to ensure that we would be financially stable and have a comfortable life in America. She wanted to give me and my brothers the best environment possible in America, so we could study and do well.

Sing Woo, twenty-seven:

I'm from Mainland China. I came to America as the first member of my family. However, like the previous migrants, I started to establish a safety cushion for my siblings. As a female and senior member of my family, I wanted to help people in my family. When I came to America, I could only read and write some English, but I could hardly engage in conversation. The skill I possessed as a textile master mechanic was not transferable. I worked at a Chinese restaurant and a Chinese bookstore and also held jobs such as a cashier at a fast-food store and a desk clerk at a hotel. I sometimes worked two jobs for sixteen hours per day, seven days per week. My brothers and sisters stayed with me when they just arrived in America. Now, the three of us are going to finish our education at the University of California.

Fumie, thirty-one:

A growing number of middle-class Japanese women, finding their status as women in Japan confined to limited educational opportunities, low paying jobs, and pressured to become traditional housewives, initiate their immigration alone. Take me. I want to be an artist. I like living in the U.S., but I don't know how long I will be here. I still wonder which is better, living in the U.S. or Japan. My income, social standing, and job were not bad at all in Japan. I don't know if I can reach my standard socially and economically in the future living in the U.S. And I don't know how much reward I can get for my hardship.

Tokiko, forty-one, a single mother:

When I saw the blue sky in California, I felt real freedom...I wanted to start my new life with my son in California. I thought America was the best place to raise my son. In Japan, people treated him piteously because he was fatherless.

Kim, nineteen:

My parents brought us to the United States from Korea, hoping to provide better educational opportunities for us. But when I see all the sacrifices and hardships they endure for our education, I can't believe they are doing this for me. My Mom, especially. I see how hard she works at the store and at home. I think Elaine Kim is right when she says, "Korean immigrant wives bear a heavier burden than Korean wives in Korea or than American wives."

"As you listen to one another, I hope you come to understand how varied the opportunities and constraints are for immigrant women here in the United States," I say. "A woman's social class determines how the woman will recreate her life here. For some immigrant women, resettlement in the U.S. empowers them, opens possibilities and new careers to them, but for most women, crossing the border and constructing new lives here is being stuck in entry-level positions, vulnerable to exploitations and harassments."

At night the task of preparing for the evening meal is no longer as easy as selecting, washing, and cooking a nutritious dinner. I unwrap the chicken, reach into the cavity, pull out the gizzards, heart, and liver, and hold the bird under running water to cleanse the inside. Patting the chicken dry, I remember Maria, a young indigenous woman from Oaxaca who guts 1000 chickens a day for Foster Farms in the Central Valley. As I slice the tomatoes, onions, green and yellow peppers, then sautee them with the chicken, words of women in San Joaquin Valley accompany my cooking.

I remember Alicia in Salinas Valley saying:

We stand here all day, packing, packing, packing from 7 a.m. to 7 p.m. We don't get breaks or lunch at all, but we have to punch out for them anyway. We are told to eat standing up.

Ester, a native of Guanajuato, now in San Joaquin Valley, told me this:

I work in an onion packing shop, and I weed and thin bell peppers, tomatoes, and onions. In the fields I can talk with other people. I don't like the onion packing shop because it is boring, and I don't like standing all day. I do not like picking bell peppers because the sun is too hot. But my job is very important; I help support my mother in Mexico.

As I set the bowl of red strawberries on the table for dessert, the warning of the migrant women in the Salinas Valley reminds me that carrots, grapes, and strawberries are coated with the most pesticides. I glance at Joanna and Joseph as I pass them the strawberries and say a quick prayer of protection for our children, for the mothers and their children who harvested the strawberries and have said:

> *Yes, we are documenting the deaths in our communities. The children are born deformed, the miscarriages, the number of people dying with cancer. The pesticides are pouring over us. We live in a toxic environment. I know the cancer is growing in my body. But it will get you, too. You eat this food.*

At the end of the day, I crawl into bed, pull the covers over me and sink my head into the down pillow. I remember meeting Ana in Michocan, Mexico, who talked of her family up north:

> *In California, everyone is working so hard for their comforts, and they do not see their families here in Mexico as much. They get all used up there, like my father, who came back with a lung disease after working in a down factory.*

I am realizing how the women crossing borders are the underpinnings of my life: they assemble the clothes I wear, the computer I write with, the sleeping bag I camp with; they harvest the food I eat, care for children and elderly, and clean houses in the neighborhood. They are the students I teach. These women moved by global labor patterns are crossing not only political boundaries, but frontiers of identity and reality in a new economic marketplace. Their words reflect the hidden side of our economy. However, my neighbor says:

> *They are not part of this society. They come to my house, they clean, and they leave by the time I'm home. And I don't have to deal with their problems. They are not part of my world.*

But I've heard other women say other things. Listening to these women, I'm reconstructing a way of looking at the world that is more multi-layered, accurate, and strangely complex.

'Liberating' Science

BY

ANDREA

SCHLUTER

⁓

When I read Deborah Skilliter's essay ("Studying Science, Playing Politics," July 13, 1994, *The Globe and Mail*), I found myself nodding in empathy with this woman's experience of blatant sexism and harassment during her study of geology. I felt the article was of particular importance because people don't really know what transpires in the revered halls of academic science. But often the discrimination, the undermining of women's power and esteem, is much more insidious than her article illustrated. I would like to put the issue of women in science into a broader context, and to discuss why, unfortunately, Ms. Skilliter's experience is not exceptional.

Recently a friend of mine delivered a marvelous defence of her doctoral thesis in botany. It was an admirable piece of work by anyone's standard. Yet at a celebration of the success later that evening, she turned to me and said in all seriousness, "Well, I sure pulled the wool over everyone's eyes."

Why did this sound so familiar to me, almost expected? This woman's research is original and meticulously carried out, her only limitations (and these are severe) are self-esteem and confidence. It recalled my own experience in the world of academic science.

Determined to be a biologist from as early as I can remember, I had taken every opportunity to work as a field assistant in the summers during my undergraduate years and as a research assistant after I graduated. I entered graduate school excited that I was going to make a major contribution to the field of ecology. Within two months, I had switched out of the PhD program and into a master's program, convinced that I did not have what it took to be a scientist.

My experience in science and that of female friends seem to show some larger dynamic that finally is being recognized. For the past three years, the prestigious journal *Science* has published an annual issue dedicated to women in science and engineering, formally recognizing the troublesome statistics. Although women make up 46 per cent of the the work force, they make up only 16 per cent of the work force in science and engineering.

There are a number of causes. First, women do not seem to thrive in the competitive atmosphere of science. The history of classical science marks it as a very male-dominated discipline, by which I mean competitive, with emphasis on selling oneself, and with great confidence in subduing and wresting the secrets of nature (identified as female, of course). I know of several groups of women that have formed within science departments to discuss scientific papers they have read. This is in addition to similar activities in the co-ed courses they take, but they report that they find the critical atmosphere of the female groups less aggressive and the reduced one-upmanship more productive to learning. It has also been noted that women professors tend to run their labs less competitively than do their male colleagues. They are more likely to encourage collaboration on a problem than to pit students against one another in a race for results.

Second, it has been argued by people such as Evelyn Fox-Keller in her book, *Reflections on Science and Gender,* and recently in the journal *Science* that there may be a feminine way of doing science that is automatically discredited because it is not classical—and therefore not valid. In classical science there is a belief in the objectivity of the observer, an assumption that does not make intuitive sense to many women.

This analytical approach has led to a mechanistic view of the natural world. Women want to allow for more ambiguity and perhaps (Heaven forbid!) less predictability. My own thesis work involved looking at whole forest communities and avoiding a traditional reductionist approach to the ecological problem at hand. How this offended members of my own and other departments! One professor remarked after a seminar I gave on a related topic: "Is this really science? Do you people in ecology really do this kind of stuff?"

In order to succeed in anything you must be able to picture yourself performing in that role. Everyone I have spoken to in science, male or female, has mentioned as a major influence in his or her success the impact of some inspiring professor. The lack of female role models is a third and serious block for women in science. Gloria Steinem in *Revolution from Within* cites a longitudinal study of 200 000 students at 300 institutions in all undergraduate categories that showed women reporting a major increase in "self-criticism" between entering and leaving college, while male students either maintained or experienced a strengthening in intellectual and personal esteem. She remarks that for many such demonstrated trends the determining factor seems to be that, with each additional year of higher education, the women see less of themselves. In my undergraduate years there was only one female professor with whom I came into contact. I was lucky that she was in my field and encouraged and employed me for a number of years. But the statistics are out for Canadian universities and the numbers of women faculty in all departments is shameful and almost unbelievable.

Fourth, women are being lost from science at all stages, even from the earliest years. Boys usually handle the equipment while the girls sit by or take observations. Boys are asked more questions and receive more eye contact than girls; a British-U.S. study cited by Ms. Steinem found that boys are five times more likely to receive a teacher's attention and eight to 12 times more likely to speak in class.

When I read this I had to laugh because I recall in Grade 5 being in a science group made up of two boys and two girls. The boys were aggressive and demanded to use the equipment and I usually demurred. But one day I was particularly interested in an experiment with electricity and insisted on trying out my ideas. This incident earned me a report card that said I was aggressive and could not get along with the boys in my group!

I believe strongly in affirmative-action programs because the only way to admit more females into the scientific realm is to have women on the hiring committees. And the only way to encourage more women into the discipline is to have more role models.

As well, perhaps the integration of men and women in science is the only way to get beyond some of the boundaries that science is up against these days. Rita Arditti, in *Feminism and Science*, wrote: "The task that seems of primary importance for women and men is to convert science from what it is today, a social institution with a conservative function and defensive stand, into a liberating and healthy activity. Science needs a soul which would show love and respect for its subjects of study and would stress harmony with the rest of the universe."

Why Men Are Hogging the Digital Highway

BY

DAVID

PLOTNIKOFF

Remember the good ol' days when the information superhighway was a mandatory topic for a cocktail party chat? Here was this shiny new medium that could level the playing field in interpersonal communications.

It could be a place where users would be judged only by their words and the intellect behind those words. The old prejudices surrounding gender, race, class and physical appearance would magically fall away and we would all speak as equals in the Temple of the Very Fast Modem.

Now here we are, just five minutes into the virtual rush hour, and already that promise is proving to be an empty one for women. Yes, women are driving the digital road in record numbers. But from small on-line communities to the 20-million-user Internet, it's estimated that more than eight of every 10 on-line citizens are male.

There are no simple explanations why women are under-represented in cyberspace. As commercial services edge closer to becoming a true mass-market phenomenon, there's a growing awareness that on-line culture is not an entirely new ball game. Virtual communities mirror the real world, with many of the old assumptions and biases intact.

What's to blame for the gender gap? Users, academics and industry watchers point to an array of social phenomena with roots that extend well beyond on-line. The real reasons may be as fundamental as the differences in the way men and women use language and the way each sex views technology.

Young girls begin getting

negative messages about technology, math and science in elementary school. Research shows boys and girls are equal in computer use until about Grade 5. After that, the boys' use rises while the girls' use falls. Studies also show that girls, regardless of ability, tend to start avoiding science and math around Grade 7.

Terry Winograd, a professor of computer science at Stanford University, says there is a complex set of social forces that may cause girls to see computers as a boys-only club. "It's probably a hundred different messages—some subtle and some not so subtle—about who has the computer and what it's used for," says Winograd.

Julia Oesterle of the Institute for Research on Learning in Palo Alto, Calif., says her 15-year-old daughter's first experience with the mostly male environment on the Prodigy service was disappointing. "She's a pretty, smart, honors-class kid and was one of few girls to hang on to playing Nintendo long after most girls abandoned it to the boys," says Oesterle. "After being on-line for a couple of nights, she lamented 'Where are the girls?'"

By the time many young women reach college, the alienation from tech has become a full-blown estrangement.

According to U.S. National Science Foundation figures, men receive 75 per cent of all computer science degrees.

The higher up the ladder, the worse it gets. Women receive between 13 and 15 per cent of the doctoral degrees awarded in computer science and less than 10 per cent of the doctorates in engineering.

That, in turn, refuels the cycle for another generation of young women growing up without female mentors in teaching positions. (One recent study estimates that 92 per cent of computer science and engineering faculty members in the U.S. are male.)

UNIX, a system of computer commands that was essential to navigating the Internet until very recently, is a perfect example of the type of knowledge women miss out on by not being "part of the club" in school. "To use UNIX you have to have gone through a kind of apprenticeship training period," says Winograd. "And that occurs in environments that aren't very hospitable to women. The route to having UNIX skills is going through a social environment that is heavily male."

For those who don't go through the "apprenticeships" in school, acquiring those digital skills later in life is much harder.

Not surprisingly, out in the working world, the types of tech professions that demand computer literacy—and often come with company-sponsored Internet access—still tend to be dominated by men. Technophobia is not an exclusively female disorder—but women in general do react negatively to technology more often than men.

A Dell Computer Corp. poll in the fall [1993] questioned 1000 adults and found 55 per cent of the women admitted discomfort with new technology, compared with 45 per cent of the men.

Beyond the educational realm, there is the persistent stereotyping of computer users as freakish, socially maladroit, sexually undesirable creatures. Add to that the mass media's sensationalistic coverage of the on-line world's darker side.

From Ann Landers' advice column to the *Village Voice,* the overwhelming message is that cyberspace is populated by cyber-stalkers, lying lotharios and perverts of every stripe. The on-line world is presented as just another place where bad men victimize helpless women.

Harassment is a bona-fide threat to every on-line citizen, regardless of gender. It can range from offensive E-mail (which can be unintentionally offensive because there are few tools in cyberspace to convey irony or sarcasm) to on-line stalking that carries over into real life.

But there is no pat definition of what separates harassment from just plain rudeness. Legal scholarship on the subject is in its infancy, and most harassment cases to date have been settled out of court.

Many women, whether they've been singled out for harassment or not, find the general atmosphere on-line to be overtly hostile. The Internet tradition of flaming (posting or mailing hostile messages) tends to make women avoid some of the most vital discussion areas in cyberspace.

There are at least two studies that say women—particularly those new to Internet culture—are most likely to perceive strident, contentious postings as personal attacks.

Susan Herring, a researcher at the University of Texas at Arlington, analyzed a year of male and female participation in two academic electronic lists. She found a small minority of males dominated the discussion on both lists.

Women who tried to participate were either targeted by flames or ignored. Topics initiated by women were less likely to be taken up by the group as a whole.

Gladys We, a master's student in communications at Simon Fraser University in Vancouver, reported last year that on the Internet men tend to dominate even the groups devoted to feminism and women's discussions. She pegged the population of the alt.feminism newsgroup as being 11 per cent women, 83 per cent men and 6 undeterminable.

The bottom line for many women may be this: They simply have neither the time nor the inclination to play around with the machine. (Playing around with the computer—exploring, experimenting and learning by making mistakes—is probably the most time-honored and effective path toward digital mastery.)

Last fall on CompuServe, a Ziffnet co-operative forum with the magazine *Working Woman* generated thousands of postings from professional women. The consensus was that women are not on-line for play. Whereas men will take the intricacies of the computer as a personal challenge, women are concerned about seeing the practical benefit of the endeavor.

As one Ziffnet-*Working Woman* participant wrote: "If you build it, they will come. If there's a subject women care about, we will be there.... Women don't tend to have gadget envy the way many guys do. They're practical and sensible and don't waste time on stuff that doesn't meet their needs."

Amy O'Donnell, manager of market research, planning and analysis for CompuServe, says her research has shown that men will often look at their home computers as either hot-rods to tinker with or a challenge to conquer. "It's like back in the '60s when men would talk about the horsepower of their cars," she says. "Now it's your computer and how much memory, how fast your modem is. Let's face it: Women just want it to work."

Kim Haskitt, an editor-publisher for a large health clinic in Seattle who's used both America Online and Compu-Serve, says she's not interested in using the services for socializing. "I've participated in (chat areas) and think they're a huge waste of time. They are childish and a virtual meat market," she says. "It just seemed like a bunch of teeny-boppers trying to do their best to impress or shock. Believe me, nothing will ever beat sitting in a café, drinking a *latté* and talking about life with a friend.

No phone, no computer software, no interactive TV, no nothing. On-line is a tool, not a hobby."

Nobody can say how the dialogue between the sexes will play out in the coming years, as on-line services become woven into the fabric of mainstream culture. It's already painfully clear that there will never be an on-line environment where gender simply disappears between the bits and bytes.

Industry types, academics and users agree that on-line will not truly be ready for prime time until women start showing up in big numbers. So what will it take to get them there? To nobody's great surprise, they seem to want pretty much the same things everyone does: convenience, ease of use and an environment where their contributions are given a fair hearing.

It's very early in the game. The major players in the on-line field are just now beginning to court the tens of millions of potential users who must come into the fold if cyber culture is to reach its full potential. In the long run, nobody will win without listening to women.

This
Is Not
Final

~

FRAN

DAVIS

(Finally after fourteen months) the names
Nathalie and Barbara and Sonia
and the heels of hunting boots
pounding the halls at five o'clock
doors of the classrooms suddenly thrown
back and he smiles (out of the newspaper cutting)
—I want the women—orders the men to leave

(Why am I trying to hear) the bullets
the men running away from the sound of shots
Maud and Hélène and Maryse
(more than a year ago I could not)
—We are only women, studying—
blood on the desks and blackboards

(I am reading again) how he went free
from floor to floor gunning down fourteen women
Annette and Barbara and Geneviève
how he shot his head off leaving
a letter threatening another fifteen

(Am I trying finally to write) the parents waiting
outside till midnight for thirteen wounded children
and waiting for Annie and Sonia and Maryse
waiting a year for the letter, for the names of the fifteen

I am trying to write the vigil on the mountain
snow falling on candles for Michèle and Anne-Marie
I am trying to write about the brutal father of Mark Lepine

I am writing fourteen months later about the gun laws
murdered wives and girlfriends found in the streets

I am writing about my own long silence, how it speaks.

Out Of the Woods

~

BY

JODI L. JACOBSON

On areas of India where the forests have been ravaged, women and children have to spend three to five hours each day just to gather enough fuel to cook the evening meal. Women there have taken to saying, "It's not what's in the pot, but what's under it, that worries you."

Their concerns are well-founded. The scarcity of leaves, twigs, branches, grasses, and other materials used for cooking fuel now rivals the scarcity of food itself as a cause of malnutrition in parts of sub-Saharan Africa, Haiti, India, Mexico, Nepal, and Thailand. The rampant loss of forests and other lands has a devastating effect on women and children throughout the developing world.

For cash-poor women, healthy forests are a savings bank from which they draw the interest—in the form of fuel, food, fodder, and countless other goods—that their families depend on to survive. As these lands become debased, the principal in the account declines, and women are forced to borrow against the future. For example, they compensate for the scarcity of fuel by, among other things, cutting live trees instead of dead ones, and cooking fewer meals. And because women are largely responsible for feeding their families, they are forced to work longer hours to make ends meet, a situation that further compromises their health and well-being and that of their children.

Given women's vast potential for helping to reverse the loss of forests, it's hard to imagine why most development programs are actually *reducing* women's access to and ownership of land. The prominent role women play in using and maintaining forests makes it not only logical, but critical, that they be included in managing forest ecosystems. But throughout Africa, Asia, and Latin America, women are being muscled out of forests—and off croplands and grasslands—by governments and private interests looking to make a quick buck through the development of "cash crops."

Women are rarely included in these plans. And as more and more of the land on which they depend is made off-limits to them, their circumstances are becoming more tenuous than ever before. Only when development strategies recognize, and are geared toward supporting the role of women in conserving forests, can we begin to solve many of the economic and environmental problems that otherwise promise to spin out of control.

Survival Stores

Forests and other land resources are to women in the Third World what grocery stores and utilities are to most women in industrialized nations. Forests, for example, are a major source of fuel for Third World homes. Without wood, women can't cook the food they've grown and harvested, or do simple things like boil water or heat their homes. Much of the Third World still depends on wood, leaves, and other forms of "biomass" for its domestic energy needs, and it usually falls to women and girls to collect this fuel—as in rural Africa, where mothers and their daughters gather 60 to 80 percent of all the fuel their families need.

Women look to the forest for other needs, too. In the woods they collect plant fibers to make cloth and thread, plants and herbs used for medicines, seeds used in condiments and oils, and many other materials. In India, women use the bark of the tendu tree to treat diarrhea.

Foods gathered from trees and bushes also add critical nutrients to the grain-based diets of people throughout the Third World. Fruits, vegetables, and nuts—important sources of vitamins, minerals, proteins, and fats—are widely used to supplement staple crops. In many areas it is the job of women to protect and manage these trees. Indonesian women harvest bananas, mangos, guavas, and avocados from 37 species of trees growing around their homes. Women often use these and other forest goods to make money for their families. In Senegal, for example, shea-nut butter made from the fruit of local trees is one of many marketable goods women produce to earn cash. Muslim women in the Middle East living in purdah (seclusion) often cultivate trees within the confines of their gardens, sending their children out to sell the fruit.

But because they are not considered major cash crops, these foods women gather and the lands that produce them often are overlooked and under-valued by development experts. A study by the United Nations Food and Agriculture Organization in northeast Zambia found that what was officially cataloged as "useless" forest land was actually a major source of leafy wild vegetables and mushrooms, as well as caterpillars, eaten by local families. Women there rely on these items as sources of protein and of cash income. In times of scarcity, tree foods often make the difference between life and death. In Tanzania, the fruits and nuts from just three types of trees provide some food for rural women every month of the year. The United Nations found that these trees were used more intensively during famines and droughts.

Forests also provide fodder for the livestock rural women keep to add milk and meat to their families' diets. In most regions, women are solely responsible for finding food for their animals.

Finally, the forests give women wood and thatch to repair homes, and the branches and logs they use to build fencing or to carve spoons, bowls, and other utensils.

The bottom line is that much of what women need to help their families survive comes from forests. When they can't turn to the land, it's anyone's guess how they will make a living.

The Real Forest Workers
Forests offer women plenty of resources for everyday life, but they also constitute a source of jobs and income. Forget Paul Bunyan and other conventional images of macho, flannel-shirted lumberjacks; in many rural areas in the Third World, women make up a big share of the labor force in logging, wood processing, nurseries, plantations, and small-scale forest products industries. They log trees to make charcoal, grow seedlings for sale, and harvest wood for carving, among other things.

And while logging is usually considered the big-money forest industry, products that contain no wood at all often play an even bigger part in local and national economies throughout the Third

World. World Bank researchers Augusta Molnar and Götz Schreiber estimate that in India, 40 percent of revenue from forests—and 75 percent of the net export earnings from forestry products—come from so-called non-wood resources. The same is true in Thailand, Indonesia, and Burma.

Poor, rural women can make a large chunk of their income, for instance, by collecting raw materials and using them to make saleable items out of bamboo, rattan, and rope. In one province in Egypt, 48 percent of the women make their living through such "minor" forest products industries. In hard times, women who don't own land and can't make enough as field workers often fall back on collecting these resources. In India, for example, about 600 000 women harvest tendu leaves in the wild for use as wrappings for domestic cigarettes.

Robbed of Resources

Imagine an American woman trying to scrape together food for herself or her children if she suddenly had no access to grocery stores or markets, and the modern dilemma of women in subsistence communities may be easier to understand. Trad-

itionally, even though African and Asian women could rarely "own" land, they usually had equal rights—as members of a community—to use community, or "commons," land according to their families' needs. However, they have always had to face restrictions on the use of land that have never applied to men.

But now even women's limited access to land is rapidly eroding, despite the fact that they depend on forests and other land resources for survival.

The "commons" lands formerly open to women increasingly are being converted to private property or turned into "open access" systems that *no one* controls. Investments by governments, donor agencies, and multinational corporations are directly encouraging communities to shift land use from community-controlled "subsistence" activities to raising cash crops. In many countries, large areas that were once communal forest have been privatized and set aside for agriculture or plantation forestry, resulting in widespread deforestation and a blow to women's ability to provide for their families.

In Zanzibar, Tanzania, commercial clove tree plantations began to replace once-communal natural forests in the late 19th century. One hundred years later, the spread of commercial agriculture continues and is creating a crisis in poor households, which now have to spend up to 40 percent of their income on the fuel they once were able to find in nearby forests. In Western Kenya, more and more land is now privately owned and thus off-limits to the poor.

And in India, much of the commons land now disappearing into government and private hands was once used by village women to secure fuel under a community system. "Contrary to the popular belief that the gathering of wood for fuel is [primarily] responsible for deforestation and fuelwood shortages," says Bina Agarwal, professor of agricultural economics at the Institute of Economic Growth in Delhi, India, "evidence [in India] points to past and ongoing state policies and schemes as significant causes."

Agarwal contends that what remains of India's forests will disappear within 45 years if the widespread conversion of sacred groves and other communal land for cash crops, dams, and commercial timber continues at today's pace.

Women won't benefit from these changes in land use, because privatization favors male landholders. Legal and cultural obstacles prevent women from obtaining titles to land, and without these titles, they can't be included in the cash crop schemes affecting forests and other lands. (Land titles invariably are given to men because governments and international agencies routinely identify them as heads of their households, regardless of whether or not they actually support their families.)

Women's rights to land are subject to the wishes of their husbands or the whims of male-dominated courts and community councils. In one region of Kenya, where women cannot own land, they also are restricted from planting trees. According to custom, control over land is determined by the ownership or planting of trees on it. Not surprisingly, men in the area have opposed women's attempts to plant more trees and other sources of fuel.

In northern Cameroon, some men only allow their wives to plant papaya trees, which are short-lived and do not count toward establishing land rights. In Nigeria, women have rights to the kernel, but not the oil, of the palm tree, which is sold by men as a cash crop.

Unfortunately, when men make more money, it rarely comes back to their families. It goes instead to unessential purchases such as radios, clothes, and alcohol. Family welfare continues to depend on what women can come up with, according to studies in every region of the Third World—making women and their children the big losers in the transition to a cash crop economy.

Forest Keepers

Women in Third World subsistence economies are the unacknowledged experts on the use and management of trees and other forest products. They know how important forests are in preserving ecosystems (forests play a critical role in replenishing fresh water supplies, for instance) and appear to be as careful in conserving forests as they are reliant on using them.

Women are more effective at protecting and regenerating the environment than either the state or private landowners, according to research on common lands conducted by Babjik Kudar, director of the Indian State Common Lands College. The reason is obvious enough. When you depend on something, you learn to take care of it.

Beyond their experience at managing forests, women's knowledge of forest resources constitutes a vast mental store of information on species that scientists regularly lament being unable to catalog. Tribal women in India, for example, know of medicinal uses for some 300 forest species. A survey in Sierra Leone found that women could name 31 products they gathered or made from nearby trees and bushes, while men could name only eight.

Unfortunately, "most forest policies and most foresters continue to overlook or ignore this diversity of knowledge," says Paula Williams, a forest and society specialist at the Institute for Current World Affairs in London. Tree-planting campaigns and international investments to stem deforestation have all but ignored women. Of 22 social forestry projects appraised by the World Bank from 1984 through 1987, only one mentioned women as a project beneficiary. And only four of 33 rural development programs that involved forestry funded by the World Bank over the same period included women in some way.

Undervaluing women's social and economic contributions is certain to slow progress toward broad social and environmental goals, such as preserving biodiversity and protecting the role played by forests in water cycles. The only real hope of saving forests and other resources is to begin providing greater economic opportunity to the women who depend on them for survival.

The Population Trap

It's an axiom of the environmental movement that population growth is a big obstacle to preserving the environment: the more people there are, the greater the demands on the Earth's resources. But few development experts consider that when a woman's basic resources are taken away, she is actually likely to want *more* children to help her shoulder the increased workload—even when the region where she lives is already home to more people than the land can realistically support.

From the perspective of a poor, rural woman, children represent an investment in the future. With few opportunities to save cash and no chance to own land, women too old to fend for themselves turn to their children for support. Children are a ready labor force. The time constraint imposed on women by the longer hours they must work to make ends meet means they lean more

heavily on the contributions of their children—especially girls.

Often, mothers are forced by circumstance to keep their daughters out of school so that they might help with the housework—ensuring that another generation of females will grow up with fewer prospects than their brothers. In Africa, for example, "more and more girls are dropping out of both primary and secondary school or just missing school altogether due to increasing poverty," says Madame Phoebe Asiyo, forest specialist at the United Nations Fund for Women.

This is the population trap. Many of the policies and programs carried out in the name of development actually increase women's dependence on children as a source of status and security. And the continued rapid population growth in Third World communities just compounds the destruction of the local environment.

To fail to recognize women's roles in forest management and as income earners is to fail in the fundamental purpose of development itself. If women in subsistence economies are the major suppliers of food, fuel, and water for their families, and yet their access to productive resources is declining, then more people will suffer from hunger, illness, and loss of productivity.

If women have learned ecologically sustainable methods of forestry, and have extensive knowledge about genetic diversity, yet are denied partnership in development, then this wisdom will be lost.

Without addressing issues of equity and justice, then, development goals that are ostensibly universal—such as the alleviation of poverty, the protection of ecosystems, and the creation of a balance between human activities and environmental resources—simply cannot be achieved.

"Many people believe," says Paula Williams, "that first we should save the world's tropical forests, then we can worry about women and children. Unless we work with women and children, however, it will be impossible to 'save' the tropical forests."

The
Poets in the
Kitchen

 ome years ago, when I was teaching a graduate seminar in fiction at Columbia University, a well known male novelist visited my class to speak on his development as a writer. In discussing his formative years, he didn't realize it but he seriously endangered his life by remarking that women writers are luckier than those of his sex because they usually spend so much time as children around their mothers and their mothers' friends in the kitchen.

What did he say that for? The women students immediately forgot about being in awe of him and began readying their attack for the question and answer period later on. Even I bristled. There again was that awful image of women locked away from the world in the kitchen with only each other to talk to, and their daughters locked in with them.

Buy my guest wasn't really being sexist or trying to be provocative or even spoiling for a fight. What he meant—when he got around to explaining himself more fully—was that, given the way children are (or were) raised in our society, with little girls kept closer to home and their mothers, the woman writer stands a better chance of being exposed, while growing up, to the kind of talk that goes on among women, more often than not in the kitchen; and that this experience gives her an edge over her male counterpart by instilling in her an appreciation for ordinary speech.

It was clear that my guest lecturer attached great importance to this, which is understandable. Common speech and the plain, work-aday words that make it up are, after all, the stock in trade of some of the best fiction writers. They are the principal means by which char-acters in a novel or story reveal themselves and give voice sometimes to profound feelings and complex ideas about themselves and the world. Perhaps the proper measure of a writer's talent is skill in rendering everyday speech—when it is appropriate to the story—as well as the ability to tap, to exploit the beauty, poetry and wisdom it often contains.

"If you say what's on your mind in the language that comes to you from your parents and your street and friends you'll probably say some-thing beautiful." Grace Paley tells this, she says, to her students at the beginning of every writing course.

It's all a matter of exposure and a training of the ear for the would-be writer in those early years of apprenticeship. And, according to my guest lecturer, this training, the best of it, often takes place in as unglamorous a setting as the kitchen.

He didn't know it, but he was essentially describing my experience as a little girl. I grew up among poets. Now they didn't look like poets —whatever that breed is supposed to look like. Nothing about them suggested that poetry was their calling. They were just a group of ordinary housewives and mothers, my mother included, who dressed in a way (shapeless housedresses, dowdy felt hats and long, dark, solemn coats) that made it impossible for me to imagine they had ever been young.

Nor did they do what poets were supposed to do—spend their days in an attic room writing verses. They never put pen to paper except to write occasionally to their relatives in Barbados. "I take my pen in hand hoping these few lines will find you in health as they leave me fair for the time being," was the way their letters invariably began. Rather, their day was spent "scrubbing floor," as they described the work they did.

Several mornings a week these unknown bards would put an apron and a pair of old house shoes in a shopping bag and take the train or streetcar from our section of Brooklyn out to Flatbush. There, those who didn't have steady jobs would wait on certain designated corners for the white housewives in the neighborhood to come along and bargain with them over pay for a day's work cleaning their houses. This was the ritual even in the winter.

Later, armed with the few dollars they had earned, which in their vocabulary became "a few raw-mouth pennies," they made their way back to our neighborhood, where they would sometimes stop off to have a cup of tea or cocoa together before going home to cook dinner for their husbands and children.

The basement kitchen of the brownstone house where my family lived was the usual gathering place. Once inside the warm safety of its walls the women threw off the drab coats and hats, seated themselves at the large center table, drank their cups of tea or cocoa, and talked. While my sister and I sat at a smaller table over in a corner doing our homework, they talked—endlessly, passionately, poetically, and with impressive range. No subject was beyond them. True, they would indulge in the usual gossip: whose husband was running with whom, whose daughter looked slightly "in the way" (pregnant) under her bridal gown as she walked down the aisle. That sort of thing. But they also tackled the great issues of the time. They were always, for example, discussing the state of the economy. It was the mid and late 30's then, and the aftershock of the Depression, with its soup lines and suicides on Wall Street, was still being felt.

Some people, they declared, didn't know how to deal with adversity. They didn't know that you had to "tie up your belly" (hold in the pain, that is) when things got rough and go on with life. They took their image from the bellyband that is tied around the stomach of a newborn baby to keep the navel pressed in.

They talked politics. Roosevelt was their hero. He had come along and rescued the country with relief and jobs, and in gratitude they christened their sons Franklin and Delano and hoped they would live up to the names.

If F.D.R. was their hero, Marcus Garvey was their God. The name of the fiery, Jamaican-born black nationalist of the 20's was constantly invoked around the table. For he had been their leader when they first came to the United States from the West Indies shortly after World War I. They had contributed to his organization, the United Negro Improvement Association (UNIA), out of their meager salaries, bought shares in his ill-fated Black Star Shipping Line, and at the height of the movement they had marched as members of his "nurses' brigade" in their white uniforms up Seventh Avenue in Harlem during the great Garvey Day parades. Garvey: He lived on through the power of their memories.

And their talk was of war and rumors of wars. They raged against World War II when it broke out in Europe, blaming it on the politicians. "It's these politicians. They're the ones always starting up all this lot of war. But what they care? It's the poor people got to suffer and mothers with their sons." If it was *their* sons, they swore they would keep them out of the Army by giving them soap to eat each day to make their hearts sound defective. Hitler? He was for them "the devil incarnate."

Then there was home. They reminisced often and at length about home. The old country. Barbados—or Bimshire, as they affectionately called it. The little Caribbean island in the sun they loved but had to leave. "Poor—poor but sweet" was the way they remembered it.

And naturally they discussed their adopted home. America came in for both good and bad marks. They lashed out at it for the racism they encountered. They took to task some of the people they worked for, especially those who gave them only a hard-boiled egg and a few spoonfuls of cottage cheese for lunch. "As if anybody can scrub floor on an egg and some cheese that don't have no taste to it!"

Yet although they caught H in "this man country," as they called America, it was nonetheless a place where "you could at least see your way to make a dollar." That much they acknowledged. They might even one day accumulate enough dollars, with both them and their husbands working, to buy the brownstone houses which, like my family, they were only leasing at that period. This was their consuming ambition: to "buy house" and to see the children through.

There was no way for me to understand it at the time, but the talk that filled the kitchen those afternoons was highly functional. It served as therapy, the cheapest kind available to my mother and her friends. Not only did it help them recover from the long wait on the corner that morning and the bargaining over their labor, it restored them to a sense of themselves and reaffirmed their self-worth. Through language they were able to overcome the humiliations of the work-day.

But more than therapy, that freewheeling, wide-ranging, exuberant talk functioned as an outlet for the tremendous creative energy they possessed. They were women in whom the need for self-expression was strong, and since language was the only vehicle readily available to them they made of it an art form that—in keeping with the African tradition in which art and life are one—was an integral part of their lives.

And their talk was a refuge. They never really ceased being baffled and overwhelmed by America—its vastness, complexity and power. Its strange customs and laws. At a level beyond words they remained fearful and in awe. Their uneasiness and fear were even reflected in their attitude toward the children they had given birth to in this country. They referred to those like myself, the little Brooklyn-born Bajans (Barbadians), as "these New York children" and complained that they couldn't discipline us properly because of the laws here. "You can't beat these children as you would like, you know, because the authorities in this place will dash you in jail for them. After all, these is New York children." Not only were we different, American, we had, as they saw it, escaped their ultimate authority.

Confronted therefore by a world they could not encompass, which even limited their rights as parents, and at the same time finding themselves permanently separated from the world they had known, they took refuge in language. "Language is the only homeland," Czeslaw Milosz, the emigré Polish writer and Nobel Laureate, has said. This is what it became for the women at the kitchen table.

It served another purpose also, I suspect. My mother and her friends were after all the female counterpart of Ralph Ellison's invisible man. Indeed, you might say they suffered a triple invisibility, being black, female and foreigners. They really didn't count in American society except as a source of cheap labor. But given the kind of women they were, they couldn't tolerate the fact of their invisibility, their powerlessness. And they fought back, using the only weapon at their command: the spoken word.

Those late afternoon conversations on a wide range of topics were a way for them to feel they exercised some measure of control over their lives and the events that shaped them. "Soully-gal, talk yuh talk!" they were always exhorting each other. "In this man world you got to take yuh mouth and make a gun!" They were in control, if only verbally and if only for the two hours or so that they remained in our house.

For me, sitting over in the corner, being seen not heard, which was the rule for children in those days, it wasn't only what the women talked about—the content—but the way they put things—their style. The insight, irony, wit and humor they brought to their stories and discussions and their poet's inventiveness and daring with language—which of course I could only sense but not define back then.

They had taken the standard English taught them in the primary schools of Barbados and transformed it into an idiom, an instrument that more adequately described them—changing around the syntax and imposing their own rhythm and accent so that the sentences were more pleasing to their ears. They added the few African sounds and words that had survived, such as the derisive suck-teeth sound and the word "yam," meaning to eat. And to make it more vivid, more in keeping with their expressive quality, they brought to bear a raft of metaphors, parables, Biblical quotations, sayings and the like:

"The sea ain' got no back door," they would say, meaning that it wasn't like a house where if there was fire you could run out the back. Meaning that it was not to be trifled with. And meaning perhaps in a larger sense that man should treat all of nature with caution and respect.

"I has read hell by heart and called every generation blessed!" They sometimes went in for hyperbole.

A woman expecting a baby was never said to be pregnant. They never used that word. Rather, she was "in the way" or, better yet, "tumbling big." "Guess who I butt up on in the market the other day tumbling big again!"

And a woman with a reputation of being too free with her sexual favors was known in their book as a "thoroughfare"—the sense of men like a steady stream of cars moving up and down the road of her life. Or she might be dubbed "a free-bee," which was my favorite of the two. I liked the image it conjured up of a woman scandalous perhaps but independent, who flitted from one flower to another in a garden of male beauties, sampling their nectar, taking her pleasure at will, the roles reversed.

And nothing, no matter how beautiful, was ever described as simply beautiful. It was always "beautiful-ugly": the beautiful-ugly dress, the beautiful-ugly house, the beautiful-ugly car. Why the word "ugly," I used to wonder, when the thing they were referring to was beautiful, and they knew it. Why the antonym, the contradiction, the linking of opposites? It used to puzzle me greatly as a child.

There is the theory in linguistics which states that the idiom of a people, the way they use language, reflects not only the most fundamental views they hold of themselves and the world but their very conception of reality. Perhaps in using the term "beautiful-ugly" to describe nearly everything, my mother and her friends were expressing what they believed to be a fundamental dualism in life: the idea that a thing is at the same time its opposite, and that these opposites, these contradictions make up the whole. But theirs was not a Manichaean brand of dualism that sees matter, flesh, the body, as inherently evil, because they constantly addressed each other as "soully-gal"—soul: spirit; gal: the body, flesh, the visible self. And it was clear from their tone that they gave one as much weight and importance as the other. They had never heard of the mind/body split.

As for God, they summed up His essential attitude in a phrase. "God," they would say, "don' love ugly and He ain' stuck on pretty."

Using everyday speech, the simple commonplace words—but always with imagination and skill—they gave voice to the most complex ideas. Flannery O'Connor would have approved of how they made ordinary language work, as she put it, "double-time," stretching, shading, deepening its meaning. Like Joseph Conrad they were always trying to infuse new life in the "old old words worn thin…by…careless usage." And the goals of their oral art were the same as his: "to make you hear, to make you feel…to make you see." This was their guiding esthetic.

By the time I was 8 or 9, I graduated from the corner of the kitchen to the neighborhood library, and thus from the spoken to the written word. The Macon Street Branch of the Brooklyn Public Library was an imposing half block long edifice of heavy gray masonry, with glass-paneled doors at the front and two tall metal torches symbolizing the light that comes of learning flanking the wide steps outside.

The inside was just as impressive. More steps—of pale marble with gleaming brass railings at the center and sides—led up to the circulation desk, and a great pendulum clock gazed down from the balcony stacks that faced the entrance. Usually stationed at the top of the steps like the guards outside Buckingham Palace was the custodian, a stern-faced West Indian type who for years, until I was old enough to obtain an adult card, would immediately shoo me with one hand into the Children's Room and with the other threaten me into silence, a finger to his lips. You would have thought he was the chief librarian and not just someone whose job it was to keep the brass polished and the clock wound. I put him in a story called "Barbados" years later and had terrible things happen to him at the end.

I sheltered from the storm of adolescence in the Macon Street library, reading voraciously, indiscriminately, everything from Jane Austen to Zane Grey, but with a special passion for the long, full-blown, richly detailed 18th- and 19th-century picaresque tales: "Tom Jones," "Great Expectations," "Vanity Fair."

But although I loved nearly everything I read and would enter fully into the lives of the characters—indeed, would cease being myself and become them—I sensed a lack after a time. Something I couldn't quite define was missing. And then one day, browsing in the poetry section, I came across a book by someone called Paul Laurence Dunbar, and opening it I found the photograph of a wistful, sad-eyed poet who to my surprise was black. I turned to a poem at random. "Little brown-baby wif spa'klin' / eyes / Come to yo' pappy an' set on his knee." Although I had a little difficulty at first with the words in dialect, the poem spoke to me as nothing I had read before of the closeness, the special relationship I had had with my father, who by then had become an ardent believer in Father Divine and gone to live in Father's "kingdom" in Harlem. Reading it helped to ease somewhat the tight knot of sorrow and longing I carried around in my chest that refused to go away. I read another poem. " 'Lias! 'Lias! Bless de Lawd! / Don' you know de day's / erbroad? / Ef you don' get up, you scamp / Dey'll be trouble in dis camp." I laughed. It reminded me of the way my mother sometimes yelled at my sister and me to get out of bed in the mornings.

And another: "Seen my lady home las' night / Jump back, honey, jump back. / Hel' huh han' an' sque'z it tight..." About love between a black man and a black woman. I had never seen that written about before and it roused in me all kinds of delicious feelings and hopes.

And I began to search then for books and stories and poems about "The Race" (as it was put back then), about my people. While not abandoning Thackeray, Fielding, Dickens and the others, I started asking the reference librarian, who was white, for books by Negro writers, although I must admit I did so at first with a feeling of shame—the shame I and many others used to experience in those days whenever the word "Negro" or "colored" came up.

No grade school literature teacher of mine had ever mentioned Dunbar or James Weldon Johnson or Langston Hughes. I didn't know that Zora Neale Hurston existed and was busy writing and being published during those years. Nor was I made aware of people like Frederick Douglass and Harriet Tubman—their spirit and example—or the great 19th-century abolitionist and feminist Sojourner Truth. There wasn't even Negro History Week when I attended P.S. 35 on Decatur Street!

What I needed, what all the kids—West Indian and native black American alike—with whom I grew up needed, was an equivalent of the Jewish shul, someplace where we could go after school—the schools that were shortchanging us—and read works by those like ourselves and learn about our history.

It was around that time also that I began harboring the dangerous thought of someday trying to write myself. Perhaps a poem about an apple tree, although I had never seen one. Or the story of a girl who could magically transplant herself to wherever she wanted to be in the world—such as Father Divine's kingdom in Harlem. Dunbar—his dark, eloquent face, his large volume of poems—permitted me to dream that I might someday write, and with something of the power with words my mother and her friends possessed.

When people at readings and writers' conferences ask me who my major influences were, they are sometimes a little disappointed when I don't immediately name the usual literary giants. True, I am indebted to those writers, white and black, whom I read during my formative years and still read for instruction and pleasure. But they were preceded in my life by another set of giants whom I always acknowledge before all others: the group of women around the table long ago. They taught me my first lessons in the narrative art. They trained my ear. They set a standard of excellence. This is why the best of my work must be attributed to them; it stands as testimony to the rich legacy of language and culture they so freely passed on to me in the wordshop of the kitchen.

Rella Braithwaite, 1923

BY

DIONNE

BRAND

My mother was born in Elmira, Ontario, in 1888; my father in 1886.

Their parents came to Canada and settled in that area called the Queen's Bush; that's where they settled. I can't say exactly, but about the time I was born we had moved a little further west.

I remember my father was telling us about how he courted my mother in a horse and buggy. My father was born in Kingston, and his father came to Canada from the West Indies—Barbados—in the 1870s; now as far as we know, they were free people when they came, and he married an American woman. They then settled there in the Queen's Bush area.

My mother's folks came up from the States; they came from the southern states to the Pennsylvania Dutch area, then on up through the northern states and then through to Canada. They came as free people, as far as we can remember back. Quite a few, quite a few Blacks were held there and came up by way of the Underground Railroad— they said that they received so much help from the Pennsylvania Dutch people.

I distinctly remember on my mother's side they had a very large farm—200 and 300 acres—'cause she's always told us. They farmed grains; I remember they'd have great big thrashings, and they were living amongst the German people. The people in that area, a great many of them were Mennonites, and even my father could speak some German. My mother said how the people were friendly, very friendly: she would say when they had these great big thrashings they always said that Mrs. Lawson—my mother's name was Mary Lawson before marriage—was such a good cook and baked so many nice pies. They would all take turns helping each other when they had these thrashings or these big jobs on the farms: the men would help each other; the women would help each other.

My mother grew up in a family of seventeen children, but she used to say, "Well, we had all the products on the farm to support ourselves." And they all helped: you didn't get very much assistance in those days.

Then, as her brothers got older, they bought farms on their own. They were bachelors; I can remember them being bachelors for many years and running their own farms. But she always mentioned the big farms that they had and the amount of food that they had produced themselves, like the milk, butter, eggs—they had plenty.

My father was an only child and he worked very hard as a labourer. He didn't really have skills when he got married and so he worked very, very hard. We had seven acres. Seven acres. We lived on that for twenty-some years, in Elmira. We moved further to Listowel, and that's where I grew up: Listowel, Ontario.

We had a great big field garden and you had to weed; I can remember, definitely, long rows up in the gardens, and then there beans that you shell, and you put them away for the winter. You'd do all these jobs.

Houses weren't insulated, not like they are today. You're cold, but you build a fire, and you sit around the fire in the morning until the house gets warm; you'd have this big stove and good heat comes out of them, but it takes a while to warm up. I was fortunate because I had both parents together all the time and we did our own home. We always owned our own home, but I think that Blacks had a harder time that were living in cities. And then, if they didn't have two parents...I was lucky because we stayed right at this one place, which was just a little frame house and seven acres. That's quite a fair amount of land.

Sometimes, in the small places like that, you sell most of what you farm, like we made our own butter and we had a separator. I helped, but the rest were older, and I can remember the oldest boys doing the separator; I was pretty small for my age so I got away without doing too much!

There had been a sizeable Black community there, but gradually they dispersed. Some of our cousins lived in the next town, so we were fortunate in that respect: we weren't all together, but we could visit. Listowel wasn't that far from Stratford; some cousins would come from Stratford and London, Ontario and other areas that our relatives lived because there was so many relatives, coming from that large family. I do remember that whole area was mainly Irish and Scotch-English.

I marvel at how my mother managed on our seven-and-a-half acres. Now we had a couple of cows and some chickens ourselves. My father didn't get home from his job on time, so she would milk those cows and do the chores, look after the chickens and that. And yet she was always involved in women's groups; she would be president of this and president of that. The Ladies Aid was quite an important one. And we went to the United Church, which was a white church, but she was always involved. After my older sisters came to the city of Toronto and got involved with the BME Church, then I can remember my mother coming down frequently to conferences and things, and we would get all the news about the Black church in Toronto.

There were seven in our family and I was the third youngest. We had four boys and three girls. It seemed very natural to her; she enjoyed all the activities, even with a family having that many children. I guess the older ones looked after the younger ones, but she was always involved.

My mother always wanted to be a schoolteacher, and I can remember her helping the various members of the family with their studying and their homework. She was quite progressive in that way. My father was self-taught, just from reading. My mother did have a fair amount of education for that time. But she was quite a progressive woman, and she was never a bored woman, even living in the country. Never bored. She was busy; she seemed to enjoy her life. But sometimes I think if I had to live in the country today, I'd probably find it depressing; but no, she was happy. She just made herself happy and I think that's what we have to do.

In the farming community where I grew up, of course, the women did not go out to work. But the area where my Black relatives lived, in the various towns, the women would be taking in laundry and going out and doing work of maids, which was prevalent in Toronto.

Now I went to high school after growing up and going through the one-room schoolhouse. My sister Dorothy—just two years younger than myself—and I, we were always the first in our class.

But at twelve years of age I found myself in the quite large high school, all white. I was quite shy 'cause I was very small for my age. I went there for a couple of years. It was quite a thing in the wintertime; I had to board in a house in town and I remember one of my older brothers helped to pay the board; I was quite anxious to go to a big city where my older sisters had gone.

Being the only Black child in the school—O Mary!—I didn't function that well. Somehow I was not impressed with strangers; I just didn't feel that comfortable.

I was born in 1923. It must be late, definitely the late '30s when I came to Toronto. By that time you would take a train, but the connections wouldn't be too good, and the money to get to travel the train—it was hard to get.

My older sisters were down in Toronto first, and I came down at the age of fifteen. Immediately, my older sister taught me how you could be a mother's helper. In the city of Toronto I was with my eldest sister—the one who's a minister, Addie—and she taught me. I was not accustomed to it—and then as soon as I got into little jobs, I attended many night classes. Very soon after that I started taking night courses and went to business college to take and learn as much as I could.

I enjoyed my childhood. As we got older, we wanted to be where there were more Blacks, but I enjoyed my childhood very much. My mother and father were both there: they lived together for over fifty years. We had close friends with the white children, but I seemed anxious to come to the big city; I was raring to come to the big city!

The first job that you could get, you took. At that time they were advertising for cook generals—and that was the older women; the older women knew how to do all the cooking and look after a household—and that's what my two older sisters were. But when you were young as my age you were a mother's helper.

Thursday was quite the day. It was a very busy day at the hairdressers'—that was women's afternoon off. There were some big dances, too, on Thursday. Special dances, seemed to me, that some of them were, and at that time they also had the midnight show.

After I got in the city and attended night classes, and I had experience, I wanted to get out of housework—being a mother's helper you did some housework with that besides looking after children. I wanted to get away from that. I tried factory and I detested that. I was at the factory at Wellington Street in Toronto; they wove some kind of twine; you operated these machines, and you walked around all day and kept these machines going, and it was very noisy. Then I worked at a place making Christmas decorations on Queen Street. This would be in the early '40s and I didn't enjoy those jobs at all, either.

It wasn't easy to get into the factory. Not easy. I think that they were just starting then getting Black women. Mainly domestic work was available. But I definitely wanted to get away from factory work after I got into that.

I think I must've been around nineteen before I got a job that I really liked. There was a place called National Selective Service, down on Queen and Spadina, and it was where the people registered for changing jobs; they'd go there to get good jobs, and I was a filing clerk there. I wasn't really typing that well, but just because I had taken typing and shorthand I was able to get a job there. Before that, of course, other places they were taking real light ones. It was a very large building. There were three Blacks there—Inez Perry, Ursula Clarke and I. A sister of mine worked in a war plant. Then after that the war was on, and I met a soldier and married at the age of twenty.

Quite a few Black people went into the service from Metro, and then many came here to Toronto from all over. It was quite the thing for these soldiers. You'd meet new soldiers on the street all the time; they tried to have some shelters and places for them at some of the churches, and some people took them into their homes.

My husband was born in Montreal of Barbadian parents and grew up in Montreal. But he was stationed at Camp Borden, so he would come to Toronto for the weekends, and that's how I met him. I think my sister met him first. She'd met a group of soldiers. She took him to one older sister's home, and then I met him. We seemed to get along. We married in 1943, quite a long time ago.

I was two months under twenty when I got married. It was different then, because they didn't concentrate on careers, and if you weren't married it would be strange. Used to be that you were an old maid or a spinster.

Nineteen forty-three was the time when most of the Blacks lived around the Spadina and Dundas and Queen area, and you scarcely went above Bloor to shop or anything: you wouldn't feel at ease and you wouldn't be treated too well; at that period of time you just felt quite out of place. At that time there were no Black businesses; the first businesses would be the barber shops and women's hairdressing. Black women's hairdressing parlours have been here for many years.

The church played a very important role, much more important than today. That's where you went to meet people. They'd even stand outside the church and socialize. In my early days I remember Mme. Brewton would teach youth on the Bible, and then she would have social functions at her home, up in North Toronto. Hew husband, Dr. Brewton, was a foot specialist and she was a beautician. She had a beautiful beauty shop on Yonge Street, and she got quite a few of us young ones involved in her Bible classes after church on Chestnut Street in Toronto.

When I first came to Toronto it was kind of nice to see all the Blacks so close together in the central area of Toronto. The Black people, we knew each other; everybody knew everybody. They were close, with the exception of a few families that were better situated and did live up a bit north. Some of the families were probably mixed, but otherwise everybody knew each other, and they really were close. Also the UAIA, which was then the UNIA, played a very important role. I went to the activities—the Saturday night dances with the records were very enjoyable. I do remember hearing a lot about Marcus Garvey at the UNIA. I wasn't at the meeting, but I can remember him coming. I remember reading about it in the *Africa Speaks* paper. I wrote for *Africa Speaks* for a while. It was a little paper.

The UNIA building was right on College Street. I had many good times there. I remember Mme. Brewton used to tell my girlfriend that we couldn't go there because you may not meet very nice people, but we enjoyed that. And the Home Service Association played an important role also.

Soldiers would go there, and they'd have socials and food. The main churches were the BME, the AME on Soho Street, which is still on Soho Street, and the Baptist, which at the beginning was on Edward Street; but during the war, there was a Reverend Stewart started a church on Elm Street, and that was a church that the soldiers would go to.

I was married. The second year of the war I was expecting a child. At that period you did not keep your job when you were expecting, but I didn't feel well from the beginning. You would feel out of place if you weren't feeling well and you were expecting, so I immediately gave my notice.

My husband was overseas a couple of years. All of the men remember that they went overseas and gave up jobs, or lost out on education and everything, and when they came back it was very hard to get a job. He retrained when he came back, along with the rest of the soldiers, but it was not easy. He remembers the long line up when they came back: nearly everybody else white and he was standing in it—he and one other Black soldier. They pointed right to my husband, and they called him up to the front, and they told him right away: "You! You go to the porters and get a job there." They just picked him out of the line up like that, but he really didn't want to go there.

Afterwards, he did train with Ryerson, but when he went to train they would tell him, "But you won't get a job at sheet metal work." It was true: at that time most Black men could only get jobs on the railroad. My husband worked as a porter for a very short time, just so many months.

Eventually we moved out here because we had one child and another on the way, and we wanted to have more space. We lived in the east end of Toronto in a flat, which was quite common at that time.

You just seemed to know where to go or not to go—the only place that you could get, it was central. The Jewish were down in that area, Beverly-McCaul. Jewish people would rent to Black people—we must remember that, we sometimes forget. A lot of them were the early type of Jews, the Jews that came from Europe, and then a lot of them were the professional people. They were the only ones that would rent to Blacks. I suppose that they remembered when they were discriminated against. Another reason was they happened to operate those businesses right down in that area: the restaurants, the doctors, everything.

My husband did get assistance from the Veterans' Land Act in buying a half-acre. He was told to look for a place and we soon found this place—a half-acre and a little house. We're still here.

When we got to Scarborough there was a new plant going up,

which was the John Mansfield plant, and he was there for three years, around 1947. He's very lucky to be alive today. He was carrying bags of asbestos, and it was the asbestos plant which just had so much bad publicity. The main number of men that worked have already passed on, so he's fortunate that he didn't stay longer than three years.

There weren't that many Blacks that came out of the city to live, so not many Black men worked there; but all the white men have gone on, and it's had an awful lot of bad publicity. At that time it was a big beautiful plant and you were so pleased to get on.

After three years, then, he was discouraged because there was no way that he could work his way up. He would see all these white friends—some of them weren't even skilled—and they would go up the ladder. After three years he left, and he started on his own in the scrap metal business, and he's still in it today, thirty-some years afterwards.

We had six children. Everybody was building their own homes or else just living in some little simple place. In those days, the women would walk out a great deal with the children and get involved in community work: the Home and School Association—they honoured me as a life time member—and Salvation Army work, all kinds of volunteer work the women here would do.

It was isolated in Scarborough—it was isolated, definitely against Blacks—but there were white friendly people. A lot of them had come here after the war too, so we all pretty well felt the same until the children would get to be teenagers, and then they would hope that Blacks wouldn't mix with them, but the people were very nice. The girls were better at finding Black activities than the boys; the boys would have more opportunities of going out with a white girl—that's always the way. The boys would be more comfortable at the parties, but the girls wouldn't be quite welcome.

When my one son was sixteen, and I was helping him with a project, I said something about using Black heroes—especially women heroes, I meant—and he said, "Were there Black heroes? I didn't know there were any women heroes." About that time I had started going to the annual September labour day function at North Buxton because my eldest sister was ministering there. "Oh, yes," I said, "I heard a lot about them when I went to North Buxton."

I had also started reading the book *Look to the North Star,* so I was collecting Black history by that time, and I got my son interested in it;

then we all got more inquisitive to find more material, and it was about that time I started working in Black history. I really couldn't find too much. Then I got the idea of writing, and I phoned *Contrast* to know if I could write those Black history columns. In 1969, I think, their paper started, and the next year I was writing a column which I kept writing for several years.

I was quite enthused when I read about Harriet Tubman. We were quite interested in all Black History, but I more or less concentrated on women because I found there was so little done. I could find quite a bit of material from the States, but there was very little done in Canada at that time, so I got quite interested in if I could contribute in some way.

The late Kay Livingstone asked me to work on a little booklet for they first Congress of Black Women, with Enid D'Oyley, and that really got me right into writing something. I still can't understand how I got into it, but I really felt strongly that you needed more material.

Many of the Black people that were here helped to pave the way for the new immigrants that come in the country. And in another respect I think we were quite conditioned: we knew the area that we could stay in, and I think it really did something to us; I think our parents were just resigned to the fact that you were discriminated against. It really does something to you because you have to survive. And so I'm very thankful for the amount of immigrants and the professional ones that have come in and inspired us.

It was good that when all the Canadian Blacks got better jobs they moved out in various areas. It was good in one way. Some of them went on, and they just forgot about their race at the same time, so that's one of the negative factors. But they definitely advanced and progressed, which was necessary—it was necessary to do that.

In the early days—the '30s, the '40s—all the women, white and black, they were deprived all right. It was years of deprivation for women. It was hard to progress, and it was difficult even for the white women to get their formal education. The boys were supposed to get the most education, because they always said the girls they didn't need it. Things have changed very much for the better for women; there's no doubt about that. As far as women abuse, I just can't seem to recall too much of that, but I'm sure it probably was kept more hidden than today. I can remember some in the Black community, but it was probably more hidden, and we weren't aware if it was going on. Today we hear of them more, but I'm sure it's easier. It's much better for all women. There's no doubt about that.

I used to read books about the women's suffrage movement and that, but it didn't seem real. I was so young, I just couldn't believe that it was that bad. Black women—we just were so busy economically, trying to make a living. They had to work, and then they had the families. Also, our men would be lowly paid—and many of our men unemployed—so women would involve themselves trying to help the home financially.

Black women always want to find our identities or know themselves better. When you speak of Black men—Black boys, we have to be very, very particular about raising our Black boys because we have too many unskilled, too many drop-outs, amongst our boys. I think there is a problem. We know right now that we are discriminated against, and it's hard enough to get work, but if they're unskilled and uneducated what hopes are there? I think once we're aware of it, we can concentrate on it more with our younger boys. It definitely does help for our Black boys to know their identity and they'll be better people for it. They just grow up so much in the white society.

When the Civil Rights movement started in the States it had quite a reaction here. Most of them beforehand were just glad to get by: you had such a hard time and our parents had a hard time, just glad to make a living. But we didn't have the pride in our race that we should've, and the Civil Rights Movement really affected Canadian Blacks: before our children would go to bed the children were all marching up and down the floor: "I'm Black and I'm proud, I'm Black and I'm proud." It was so funny when I think back. I remember that there was a whole awakening here—it really hit here in Canada, very strongly, about the pride of being Black. I think that was a necessary factor.

Listening... an Interview with Bertha Petiquan

BY

MARK DOWIE

ertha Petiquan was born Ahqweengeesikwe in 1918, a year of turmoil and deep sadness for the Wabauskang band of the Anishinabe. In a few days a hundred of the Wabauskang band (which never numbered more than 1000) were wiped out by smallpox. It was such a terrifying experience that most of the band fled the shores of Wabauskang Lake, about 400 miles northwest of Lake Superior, and scattered throughout the Great Lakes region.

Bertha's mother died of the pox two days after her daughter's birth, and Bertha was sent by her father to live with her "auntie" at a nearby lake. Aunt Sophie and her husband raised Bertha in the traditional ways of the Ojibway. She was taught the legends and medicines of her people and learned to hunt, fish, trap and gather. At 75 she still does them all, almost every day.

Unlike most of the band, Bertha never left the flat, rocky, wooded wilderness surrounding Wabauskang Lake. From her aunt, uncle and grandfather, a legendary healer named Baptiste Petiquan, she learned to hunt the moose and deer, fish the walleye, trout and muskie, trap the rabbits, marten, beaver, fox and porcupine, and revere the bear and eagle. From the banks of streams that link the myriad tiny lakes that speckle the Precambrian Shield she still gathers medicinal plants, rice, tubers, wild blueberries, cranberries, chokecherries, and raspberries, and preserves them for winter food.

How did she learn so many skills, particularly those skills that were traditionally taught only to men?

"I watched."

To this day the tiny, muscular mother of seven sits alone by the shores of rivers and lakes and watches animals feed, rut, fight and play. Her weathered face beams with delight as she recounts the seasons she has spent near the den of a mother wolf, watching her raise litter after litter of healthy pups, some of whom she is sure she has trapped in years that followed—without remorse. Killing animals for sustenance has always been part of life to the Anishinaabeg.

Recently she built a two room cabin at Lake Wabauskang. Though it's barely large enough for one person, it is stuffed with the tools and provisions of survival—traps, guns, canned preserves, huge jars of moose jerky and a freezer that takes up half the kitchen—and there are almost always a few visitors sitting around the wood stove. In the dead of winter, outside the tiny window by the old worn couch, the whole world seems black and white. There is no sound but the wind, nor a sign of life.

Once she was settled in, Bertha began searching for members and descendants of her band, issuing a call for them to return, resettle the reserve, and live off the land as she does. One by one, from as far away as Vancouver, British Columbia, they have come back to their roots, to a simple life and to pow-wows, which Bertha often leads. She is the undisputed visionary of the revitalized Wabauskang band. Two years ago there were 17 people, today there are over 50 living in her village.

Bertha's call to tradition isn't the only thing that draws them back. She has provided jobs not in gambling, uranium mining or any of the white man's industries that seek out cheap resources and labor on Indian reservations, but in sustainable-yield agriculture. The blueberries that still grow wild around the lake, and would otherwise fall to the ground, are harvested and made into jam, syrup and fruit leather at a processing plant that Bertha built with the help of younger bodies. It's a small plant by modern food processing standards, containing a walk-in freezer and refrigerator, a cooking and packing room and a single office. But it passes all the necessary government requirements. To Bertha it's the world headquarters of Wabauskang Wildfruits, and the salvation of her kin. With wild rice harvesting and a little logging (to clear land for wild berries) she has kept unemployment on the reserve at zero.

She speaks a little English but prefers to converse in Ojibway. Her daughter Jenny translates. My first question, about wilderness, is met with complete silence.

"There is no word for wilderness in Ojibway," says Jenny struggling to interpret my question.

What about "wild"?

"No word for that either."

"No wild animals"?

Jenny converses quietly with her mother for a few minutes. They chuckle as my bizarre concept of wildness is fathomed. Finally Jenny answers my question.

"Bertha says that there are a few unpredictable animals that have somehow gone mad or have rabies, but there are no wild animals. There are only wild people, and wild places—like cities. Wild people live in cities." Bertha speaks again, and Jenny adds: "But not all wild people live in cities. My cousin, for example, who lives on the reserve and kills more moose than he needs. He sells the best parts of the moose to people in town and leaves the rest to waste in the woods: he's wild." More chuckles. "He was OK before he left the reserve and went to Winnipeg. When he came back he was wild."

Is there wild land?

Land itself is never wild, she says only what is on it—El Paso, Texas for example, where she traveled a few years ago to visit Jenny and her family. It was an experience she has no interest in repeating. She won't have to, of course. Jenny is home.

Will land support people who don't respect it?

Her response comes in a long, convoluted story about Weesakayjac, a mythical Chaplinesque figure from Ojibway lore. The wise but awkward explorer attempts to find his way home through the woods, seeking direction from animals he converses with as freely as if they were human. Along the way he trips, falls, stumbles, slides, gets lost, climbs, falls again and eventually finds his destination. But not before he was able to walk on water, a skill that he acquired after a muskrat came to him in a dream. "It's true," says Bertha, her eyes wide, her hand hiding a grin. "The day after you dream of the muskrat, you can walk on water. Try it." The story is told with sweeping hand gestures and much laughter. An affirmative answer to my question about land is in there somewhere, for each of Weesakayjac's calamities teach respect for the land, which of course returns the favor by granting him safe passage home.

Which animals does she trap in the winter?

The question startles her. She grabs her coat and leads me out the door. We head into the bush. She had completely forgotten that one of her traplines needs immediate attention. This particular line is for rabbits, a staple in her winter diet. Every few feet there are tracks in the snow crossing the trail she has worn with her tiny feet.

"Wolf" says Bertha pointing to the first tracks. "Marten" to the next. "Otter...going to have babies soon," she says pointing to a smooth crease in the snow where the otter had dragged her pregnant belly. "Young wolf chasing rabbit," she says pointing with a stick to the rabbit's tracks interspersed with the small shallow imprints of the pursuing wolf. We move on to the next. "Ah, rabbit." She leaves the trail, breaking through snow up to her waist, and sets a snare a few yards away on the rabbit trail (mikana)—the word in Ojibway—for which, she says, is the same as the word for highway.

What about the highway we drove up on? (Built through the Wabauskang reserve 30 or so years ago to gain access to a gold mine 50 miles north.)

"No one told us the road was coming," she said, "and no one told us why they were building it." Though it brought loggers, miners, white hunters and eventually the drug traffickers that have devastated a whole generation of young Ojibways, Bertha seems sanguine about the road, which she uses as a pathway (mikana) to her traplines.

Back at her cabin Bertha explains why, in the face of lower fur prices and a worldwide movement against the practice, she continues to trap animals. "For food. I eat or share everything I trap...except marten and otter which I feed to the dogs."

"You eat beaver?" I ask.

"Yes."

And muskrat?

"Oh, yes. Muskrat is very good for you. They eat calamus, a medicine for colds. It's in their meat."

How does she know that muskrats eat calamus?

"I watch them."

As I look out the window of Bertha's tiny cabin to the stark shore across the frozen surface of Lake Wabauskang, it's hard to imagine a place more wild or remote. Yet Bertha speaks of her need to get away from it all.

"There is too much happening here, too much noise." I listen, but hear only silence. So where would she go? To her trapping cabin on Mystery Lake, a one room log shelter surrounded by golden aspen. It sits with grass growing out of the roof, no door, no electricity, the only structure on Mystery Lake. It's about a day's journey from Wabauskang by canoe and portage.

Bertha escapes to the cabin at least once a year, sets a fishing net and a few traps, and stays for a week or more. "I sometimes take one of my daughters, or a granddaughter, or a woman friend, but never men or boys. Best of all, I like to be alone."

The Rites of Sisterhood

BY

NAOMI

WOLF

This essay is adapted from a commencement speech delivered in 1992 by the author at Scripps College, a women's college in Claremont, California.

Guillotine joke:

Once there was revolution. Three revolutionaries were charged with treason—two men and a woman. The first revolutionary was taken to the guillotine. He was asked, "Do you want to die facing up or down?" "I'll face down." The headsman pulls the string—nothing happens. The crowd says, "It's a miracle! Set him free!" The second man approaches the block and, given the same choice, he opts to face the ground. Again when the headsman pulls the string, nothing happens and the crowd cheers to set him free. The third revolutionary replies, "I'll face up." Headsman pulls string—nothing happens! She points upward and says, "I think I see what the problem is."

Even the best of revolutions can go awry when we begin to internalize the attitudes that we are fighting. During the past twenty years women have gained legal and reproductive rights as never before, have entered new jobs and professions. At the same time, anorexia and bulimia became epidemic; sexual assaults against women are at a record high, up 59 percent from last year; Roe v. Wade *is about to be* reconsidered in the Supreme Court; the weight of fashion models and Miss Americas plummeted, from 8 percent below the weight of the average American woman to 23 percent below. And the blonde joke is enjoying a renaissance.

You are graduating in the midst of a violent backlash against the advances women have made over the last twenty years. This backlash is taking many forms, from the sudden relevance of quotes from The Exorcist *in Senate hearing rooms to beer commercials with the Swedish bikini team. What I want to give you today is a survival kit for the backlash into which you are about to graduate, a sort of five-step program to keep the dragons from taking up residence inside your own heads.*

First, let me tell you why it's so important for me to have been asked here today. My own graduation was the Commencement from Hell, an exercise in female disempowerment. I graduated eight years ago from Yale. The speaker was Dick Cavett, for little more reason than that he had been the college president's brother in an all-male secret society when they were both undergraduates. While the president was withdrawing college funds from South African investment, he was blind to the gender apartheid that he was endorsing on his own well-tended lawns.

Cavett took the microphone and seemed visibly to pale at the sight of two thousand female about-to-be Yale graduates. "When I was an undergraduate," he said, "there were no women here. The women went to Vassar. At Vassar," he said, "they had nude photographs taken of the women to check their posture in gym class. One year some of the photos were stolen, and they showed up for sale in New Haven's red-light district." His punch line? "The photos found no buyers."

I will never forget that moment. There were our parents and grandparents, many of whom had come long distances at great expense to be with us on our special day. There were we, silent in our black gowns, our tassels, our new shoes. We did not dare break the silence with boos or hisses, out of respect for our families who had given so much to make that day a success; and they in turn kept silent out of the same concern for us. Whether or not it was conscious, Cavett at that moment was using the beauty myth as it is often used in backlash: whenever *women get too close to masculine power, someone will draw critical attention to their bodies. Confronted with two thousand women who were about to become just as qualified as he himself was, his subtext was clear: you may be Elis, but you still wouldn't make pornography worth the buying.*

That day, three thousand men were confirmed in the power of a powerful institution. But many of the two thousand women felt the shame of the powerless; the choking on silence, the complicity, the helplessness. We were orphaned from our institution at that moment— or rather, that moment laid bare the way in which the sons were truly sons all along, but the daughters were there on sufferance, intellectual and spiritual foster children whose membership in the family depend- ed on self-effacement.

Commencement should be a rite of passage that makes you feel the opposite of how my graduation made me feel. My graduation did not celebrate in any way my wisdom and maturation as a woman; rather, it was a condescending pat on the head for having managed to "pass" for four years, in intellectual terms, as one of the boys.

So I want to give you the commencement talk I was denied. Since I'm only eight years older than you and still figuring things out myself, I don't feel comfortable using the second-person imperative in a way that would pretend that I have all the answers for your life. What I do when I say "you" is send a message back to my twenty-one- year-old self with the information I wish I had taken. As Gloria Steinem says, "we teach what we need to learn."

MESSAGE #1: *The first message in your survival kit is to* cherish a new definition of what it means to "become a woman." *Today, you have ended your apprenticeship into the state of adult womanhood; today, you have "become women."*

But that sounds terribly odd in ordinary usage, doesn't it? What is usually meant by the phrase "You're a real woman now"? Most con- notations are biological: you "become a woman" when you menstruate for the first time, or when you lose your virginity, when you have a child. Sometimes people say "a real woman" to suggest decorative- ness—a real woman wears a DD-cup bra—or a state of matrimony: a man can make a "real" or "honest" woman out of someone by marrying her.

These merely endocrinological definitions of becoming a woman are very different from how we say boys become men. Someone

*"becomes a man" when he undertakes responsibility or successfully
completes a dangerous quest. Let us make a new definition of "becoming
a woman" that includes the fact that you, too, no less and in some
ways more than your brothers and male friends graduating today,
have not moved from childhood to adulthood by biological maturation
alone but through your own successful completion of a struggle with
new responsibilities—a difficult, ultimately solitary quest for the adult
self.*

*But we have no archetypes for the questing young woman, her
separation from home and family, her trials by fire. We lack words for
how you become a woman through the chrysalis of education, the
difficult passage from one book, one idea, to the next. My commencement
pitted my scholarship and my gender against each other. We
need a definition of "becoming a woman" in which a scholar learns
womanhood and a woman learns scholarship, each term informing the
other; Plato and Hegel, Djuna Barnes and particle physics, mediated
to their own enrichment through the eyes and brain of the female body
with its wisdoms and its gifts.*

*When I say that you have already showed courage in earning your
B.A.'s and passing through the forest, I am not talking about the
demons of footnotes and poststructuralism. I'm talking about the extra
lessons you had outside the classroom as well as in. Many of you
graduate today in spite of the posttraumatic stress syndrome that
follows acquaintance rape, which on campuses across America one-
fourth of female undergraduates undergo. Many of you earned your
credits while surviving on eight hundred calories a day, weak from
ketosis and so faint from the anorexia that strikes one undergraduate
woman in ten that it took every last ounce of your will to get your
work in. Up to five times that number graduate today in spite of the
crushing shame of bulimia, which consumes enormous energy and
destroys self-esteem. You managed to stay focused on political theory
and Greek while negotiating private lives through a minefield of new
strains of VD, a 30 percent chlamydia rate among U.S. undergraduates,
and the ascending shadow of HIV and AIDS. You had the force of
imagination to believe that Emily Dickinson and Jane Austen still had
something to say to you while your airwaves flickered with ever more
baroque and ingenious forms of glamorized violence against women.*

*Not to mention the more mundane trials of undergraduate life. You
fell in love, fell in love with the wrong person, fell out of love, and*

survived love triangles, intrigues, betrayals, and jealousies. You took false starts in finding your life's work. Perhaps you questioned your religious assumptions, lost spiritual faith, found it again in forms that might alarm your grandparents, and lost it again to find it elsewhere anew. You lived through cliques, gossip, friends who borrowed your clothes and ruined them, dates from the Black Lagoon, money worries, second jobs, college loans, wardrobe angst, a Gulf war, earthquakes, and the way you break out magically just when you have an important job interview.

You made friends with people much richer or much poorer than your own families, and I trust that made you question how fairly this country distributes its wealth. You made friends with people of other racial and religious backgrounds and sexual affiliations than yourself, which I trust made you face the racism and homophobia that this culture embeds in all of our subconsciouses.

In earning your B.A.'s while fighting these battles so often labeled trivial, you have already proven that you are the triumphant survivors you will continue to have to be as you make your way through the backlash landscape outside this community. You have "become wo-men," and as women, your commencement is not just a beginning but a confirmation of achievement. I applaud you.

MESSAGE #2 *in your kit is the ultimate taboo subject for women. It makes grown women blush and fidget, and no, it's not sex. It's money.* Ask for money in your lives. *Expect it. Own it. Learn to use it. One of the most disempowering lessons we learn as little girls is the fear of money—that it's not nice, or feminine, to ensure that we are paid fairly for honest work. Meanwhile, women make fifty-nine cents for every male dollar and half of marriages end in divorce, at which point women's standard of living drops 43 percent. To cling to ignorance about money is to be gender illiterate.*

Of course you must never choose a profession for material or status reasons, unless you want to guarantee your unhappiness. But, for God's sake, whatever field your heart chooses, get the highest, most specialized training in it you can and hold out hard for just compen-sation. You owe it to your daughters to fight a system that is happy to assign you to the class of highly competent, grossly underpaid women who run the show while others get the cash and the credit. Once you get your hands on every resource that is due to you, organize with other women for a better deal for the supports women need in the workplace—the parental leave and child care that European women take for granted, and that we need if we are to be what almost every man assumes he can be: both a parent and a worker.

Get the highest salary you can not out of selfish greed but so that you can tithe your income to women's political organizations, shelters, crisis lines, cultural events, and universities. Ten percent is a good guideline that I use myself. When you have equity, you have influence as sponsors, shareholders, trustees, and alumnae to force institutions into positive change. Male-dominated or racist institutions won't give up power if we are sweet and patient; the only language the status quo understands is money, votes, and public embarrassment. Use your clout to open opportunities to the women of all colors and classes who deserve the education and the training you had. As a woman, your B.A. and the income it represents don't belong to you alone, just as, in the Native American tradition, the earth doesn't belong to its present occupants alone. Your education was lent to you by women of the past who made it possible for you to have it; and it is your job to give some back to living women, as well as to your unborn daughters seven generations from now.

MESSAGE #3: Never cook for or sleep with anyone who routinely puts you down.

MESSAGE #4: Honor your foremothers, *literal and metaphorical. Ask your mom or grandmother about her own life story, her own quest as she defines it. Read biographies of women of the past that you admire. Knowing how hard women worked because they believed in you will remind you, in dark moments, just how precious your freedom—and hence you—really are.*

MESSAGE #5: Give yourself the gift of speech; *become goddesses of disobedience. Sixty years ago Virginia Woolf wrote that we need to slay the Angel in the House, the self-sacrificing, compliant impulse in our own minds. It's still true. Across America, I meet young women who tell me stories of profound injustice: rape cover-ups on campus, blatant sexism in the classroom, discriminatory hiring and admission policies. When I suggest proven strategies to confront the injustice— like holding a press conference about campus crimes if the administration* is unwilling to listen—they freeze at the suggestion, paralyzed into niceness. Their eyes take on a distant look, half longing, half petrified. If only! They laugh nervously. They would, but...people would get mad at them, they'd be called aggressive, the dean would hate their guts, the trustees might disapprove.

We are taught that the very worst thing we can do is cause conflict, even in the service of doing what is right. Antigone, you will remember, is imprisoned; Joan of Arc burns at the stake; and someone might call us unfeminine! Outrage, which we would not hesitate to express on behalf of a child, we are terrified of showing on behalf of ourselves, or other women.

This fear of not being liked is a big dragon in my own life. I saw the depths of my own paralysis by niceness when I wrote a book that caused controversy. The Beauty Myth argues that rigid ideals of beauty are part of the backlash against feminism, designed to lower women's self-esteem for a political purpose. While I meant every word I said, and while enormous positive changes followed, from heightened awareness about eating disorders to an FDA crackdown on breast implants, all of that would dwindle into insignificance when someone yelled at me—as plastic surgeons, for instance, often did on television. I would sob on my boyfriend's shoulder, People are mad at me! (Of course they were mad; a three-hundred-million-dollar industry was at stake.)

Halfway through the slings and arrows, I read something by African-American poet Audre Lorde that set me free to speak truth to power without blaming myself when power got a little annoyed.

Lorde was diagnosed with breast cancer. "I was going to die," she wrote, "sooner or later, whether or not I had ever spoken myself. My silences had not protected me. Your silence will not protect you. But for every real word spoken, I had made contact with other women while we examined words to fit a world in which we all believed...What are the words you do not yet have? What are the tyrannies you swallow day by day and attempt to make your own, until you will sicken and die of them, still in silence? We have been socialized to respect fear more than our own need for language."

So I began to ask, at every skirmish: "What's the worst that could happen to me if I tell this truth?" The fact is that the backlash greatly exaggerates the consequences of our speaking. Unlike women in other countries, our breaking silence is unlikely to land us in jail and *tortured, or beaten with firehoses, or "disappeared," or run off the road at midnight. Our speaking out will make some people irritated, disrupt some dinner parties (and doubtless make them livelier), get us called names and ridiculed. And then our speaking out will permit other women to speak, and others, until laws are changed and lives are saved and the world is altered forever.*

So I wish upon you the ability to distinguish between silencings. Some are real: if you will lose your livelihood or get the life beat out of you. You will respect the necessity of the circumstance at that moment and then organize like hell so you are not faced with it again. But then there are the other 90 percent, the petty, day-to-day silencings, like when you are being hassled by some drunken guests in a hotel and, rather than confronting them, the front desk tells you to lock yourself in your room. Or when your male classmates make sexist jokes. You know when you last swallowed your words.

Next time, ask yourself: What's the worst that will happen? So you might get called a bitch, or aggressive, or a slut, or the hostess will try to change the subject, or you might have to have a long talk with your male friends. Then, each time you are silenced, push yourself a little further than you think you dare to go. It will get easier and easier.

Then, once you are not immobilized with niceness, you know what? People will *yell at you. They* will *interrupt, put you down, try to make you feel small, and suggest it's a personal problem. And the world won't end. And you will grow stronger by the day and find you have fallen in love with your own vision of the world, which you may never have known you had, because you were trying so hard not to know what you knew. And you will lose some friends and some lovers, and find you don't miss them; and new ones will find you. And you will still go dancing all night, still flirt and dress up and party, because as Emma Goldman said, "If I can't dance, it's not my revolution." And as time goes on you will know with surpassing certainty that there is only one thing more dangerous and frightening and harmful to your well-being than speaking your truth. And that is the certain psychic death of not speaking.*

A New Vision of Masculinity

BY

COOPER THOMPSON

I was once asked by a teacher in a suburban high school to give a guest presentation on male roles. She hoped that I might help her deal with four boys who exercised extraordinary control over the other boys in the class. Using ridicule and their status as physically imposing athletes, these four wrestlers had succeeded in stifling the participation of the other boys, who were reluctant to make comments in class discussions.

As a class we talked about the ways in which boys got status at school and how they got put down by others. I was told that the most humiliating put-down was being called a "fag." The list of behaviors which could elicit ridicule filled two large chalkboards, and it was detailed and comprehensive; I got the sense that a boy in this school had to conform to rigid, narrow standards of masculinity to avoid being called a fag. I, too, felt this pressure and became very conscious of my mannerisms in front of the group. Partly from exasperation, I decided to test the seriousness of these assertions. Since one of the four boys had some streaks of pink in his shirt, and since he had told me that wearing pink was grounds for being called a fag, I told him that I thought he was a fag. Instead of laughing, he said, "I'm going to kill you."

Such is the stereotypic definition of strength that is associated with masculinity. But it is a very limited definition of strength, one based on dominance and control and acquired through the humiliation and degradation of others.

Contrast this with a view of strength offered by Pam McAllister in her introduction to

Reweaving the Web of Life:

The 'Strength' card in any Tarot deck depicts, not a warrior going off to battle with his armor and his mighty sword, but a woman stroking a lion. The woman has not slain the lion nor maced it, not netted it, nor has she put on it a muzzle or a leash. And though the lion clearly has teeth and long sharp claws, the woman is not hiding, nor has she sought a protector, nor has she grown muscles. She doesn't appear to be talking to the lion, nor flattering it, nor tossing it fresh meat to distract its hungry jaws.

The woman on the 'Strength' card wears a flowing white dress and a garland of flowers. With one hand she cups the lion's jaws, with the other she caresses its nose. The lion on the card has big yellow eyes and a long red tongue curling out of its mouth. One paw is lifted and the mane falls in thick red curls across its broad torso. The woman. The lion. Together they depict strength.

This image of strength stands in direct contrast to the strength embodied in the actions of the four wrestlers. The collective strength of the woman and the lion is a strength unknown in a system of traditional male values. Other human qualities are equally foreign to a traditional conception of masculinity. In workshops I've offered on the male role stereotype, teachers and other school personnel easily generate lists of attitudes and behaviors which boys typically seem to not learn. Included in this list are being supportive and nurturant, accepting one's vulnerability and being able to ask for help, valuing women and "women's work," understanding and expressing emotions (except for anger), the ability to empathize with and empower other people, and learning to resolve conflict in non-aggressive, non-competitive ways.

Learning Violence

All of this should come as no surprise. Traditional definitions of masculinity include attributes such as independence, pride, resiliency, self-control, and physical strength. This is precisely the image of the Marlboro man, and to some extent, these are desirable attributes for boys and girls. But masculinity goes beyond these qualities to stress competitiveness, toughness, aggressiveness, and power. In this context, threats to one's status, however small, cannot be avoided or taken lightly. If a boy is called a fag, it means that he is perceived as weak or timid—and therefore not masculine enough for his peers. There is enormous pressure for him to fight back. Not being tough at these moments only proves the allegation.

Violence is learned not just as a way for boys to defend allegations that they are feminized, but as an effective, appropriate way for them to normally behave. In "The Civic Advocacy of Violence" [M. Spring 1982] Wayne Ewing clearly states:

I used to think that we simply tolerated and permitted male abusiveness in our society. I have now come to understand rather, that we advocate physical violence. Violence is presented as effective. Violence is taught as the normal, appropriate and necessary behavior of power and control. Analyses which interweave advocacy of male violence with 'SuperBowl Culture' have never been refuted. Civic expectations—translated into professionalism, financial commitments, city planning for recreational space, the raising of male children for competitive sport, the corporate ethics of business ownership of athletic teams, profiteering on entertainment— all result in the monument of the National Football League, symbol and reality at once of the advocacy of violence.

Ultimately, violence is the tool which maintains what I believe are the two most critical socializing forces in a boy's life: *homophobia*, the hatred of gay men (who are stereotyped as feminine) or those men believed to be gay, as well as the fear of being perceived as gay; and *misogyny,* the hatred of women. The two forces are targeted at different classes of victims, but they are really just the flip sides of the same coin. Homophobia is the hatred of feminine qualities in men while misogyny is the hatred of feminine qualities in women. The boy who is called a fag is the target of other boys' homophobia as well as the victim of his own homophobia. While the overt message is the absolute need to avoid being feminized, the implication is that females— and all that they traditionally represent—are contemptible. The United States Marines have a philosophy which conveniently combines homophobia and misogyny in the belief that "When you want to create a group of male killers, you kill 'the woman' in them."

The pressures of homophobia and misogyny in boys' lives have been poignantly demonstrated to me each time that I have repeated a simple yet provocative activity with students. I ask them to answer the question, "If you woke up tomorrow and discovered that you were the opposite sex from the one you are now, how would you and your life be different?" Girls consistently indicate that there are clear advantages to being a boy—from increased independence and career opportunities to decreased risks of physical and sexual assault—and eagerly answer the question. But boys often express disgust at this possibility and even refuse sometimes to answer the question. In her reports of a broad-based survey using this question, Alice Baumgartner reports the following response as typical of boys: "If I were a girl, I'd be stupid and weak as a string;" "I would have to wear makeup, cook, be a mother, and yuckky stuff like that;" "I would have to hate snakes. Everything would be miserable;" "If I were a girl, I'd kill myself."

The Costs of Masculinity

The costs associated with a traditional view of masculinity are enormous, and the damage occurs at both personal and societal levels. The belief that a boy should be tough (aggressive, competitive, and daring) can create emotional pain for him. While a few boys experience short-term success for their toughness, there is little security in the long run. Instead, it leads to a series of challenges which few, if any, boys ultimately win. There is no security in being at the top when so many other boys are competing for the same status. Toughness also leads to increased chances of stress, physical injury, and even early death. It is considered manly to take extreme physical risks and voluntarily engage in combative, hostile activities.

The flip side of toughness—nurturance—is not a quality perceived as masculine and thus not valued. Because of this boys and men experience a greater emotional distance from other people and few opportunities to participate in meaningful inter-personal relationships. Studies consistently show that fathers spend very small amounts of time interacting with their children. In addition, men report that they seldom have intimate relationships with other men, reflecting their homophobia. They are afraid of getting too close and don't know how to take down the walls that they have built between themselves.

As boys grow older and accept adult roles, the larger social costs of masculinity clearly emerge. Most women experience male resistance to an expansion of women's roles; one of the assumptions of traditional masculinity is the belief that women should be subordinate to men. The consequence is that men are often not willing to accept females as equal, competent partners in personal and professional settings. Whether the setting is a sexual relationship, the family, the streets, or the battlefield, men are continuously engaged in efforts to dominate. Statistics on child abuse consistently indicate that the vast majority of abusers are men, and that there is no "typical" abuser. Rape may be the fastest growing crime in the United States. And it is men, regardless of nationality who provoke and sustain war. In short, traditional masculinity is life threatening.

New Socialization For Boys
Masculinity, like many other human traits, is determined by both biological and environmental factors. While some believe that biological factors are significant in shaping some masculine behavior, there is undeniable evidence that cultural and environmental factors are strong enough to override biological impulses. What is it, then, that we should be teaching boys about being a man in a modern world?

- Boys must learn to accept their vulnerability, learn to express a range of emotions such as fear and sadness, and learn to ask for help and support in appropriate situations.

- Boys must learn to be gentle, nurturant, cooperative and communicative, and in particular, learn non-violent means of resolving conflicts.

- Boys must learn to accept those attitudes and behaviors which have traditionally been labeled feminine as necessary for full human development—thereby reducing homophobia and misogyny. This is tantamount to teaching boys to love other boys and girls.

Certain qualities like courage, physical strength, and independence, which are traditionally associated with masculinity, are indeed positive qualities for males, provided that they are not manifested in obsessive ways nor used to exploit or dominate others. It is not necessary to completely disregard or unlearn what is traditionally called masculine. I believe, however, that the three areas above are crucial for developing a broader view of masculinity, one which is healthier for all life.

These three areas are equally crucial for reducing aggressive, violent behavior among boys and men. Males must learn to cherish life for the sake of their *own* wholeness as human beings, not just *for* their children, friends, and lovers. If males were more nurturant, they would be less likely to hurt those they love....

Where will this change in socialization occur? In his first few years, most of a boy's learning about masculinity comes from the influences of parents, siblings and images of masculinity such as those found on television. Massive efforts will be needed to make changes here. But at older ages, school curriculum and the school environment provide powerful reinforcing images of traditional masculinity. This reinforcement occurs through a variety of channels, including curriculum content, role modeling, and extracurricular activities, especially competitive sports.

School athletics are a microcosm of the socialization of male values. While participation in competitive activities can be enjoyable and healthy, it too easily becomes a lesson in the need for toughness, invulnerability, and dominance. Athletes learn to ignore their own injuries and pain and instead try to injure and inflict pain on others in their attempts to win, regardless of the cost to themselves or their opponents. Yet the lessons learned in athletics are believed to be vital for full and complete masculine development, and as a model for problem-solving in other areas of life.

In addition to encouraging traditional male values, schools provide too few experiences in nurturance, cooperation, negotiation, non-violent conflict resolution, and strategies for empathizing with and empowering others. Schools should become places where boys have the opportunity to learn these skills; clearly, they won't learn them on the street, from peers, or on television.

Setting New Examples

Despite the pressures on men to display their masculinity in traditional ways, there are examples of men and boys who are changing. "Fathering" is one example of a positive change. In recent years, there has been a popular emphasis on child-care activities, with men becoming more involved in providing care to children, both professionally and as fathers. This is a clear shift from the more traditional view that child rearing should be delegated to women and is not an appropriate activity for men.

For all of the male resistance it has generated, the Women's Liberation Movement has at least provided a stimulus for some men to accept women as equal partners in most areas of life. These are the men who have chosen to learn and grow from women's experiences and together with women are creating new norms for relationships. Popular literature and research on male sex roles is expanding, reflecting a wider interest in masculinity. Weekly news magazines such as *Time* and *Newsweek* have run major stories on the "new masculinity," suggesting that positive changes are taking place in the home and in the workplace. Small groups of men scattered around the country have organized against pornography, battering and sexual assault. Finally there is the National Organization for Changing Men which has a pro-feminist, pro-gay, pro-"new man" agenda, and its ranks are slowly growing.

In schools where I have worked with teachers, they report that years of efforts to enhance educational opportunities for girls have also had some positive effects on boys. The boys seem more tolerant of girls' participation in co-ed sports activities and in traditionally male shops and courses. They seem to have a greater respect for the accomplishments of women through women's contributions to literature and history. Among elementary school aged males, the expression of vulnerable feelings is gaining acceptance. In general, however, there has been far to little attention paid to redirecting male role development.

Boys Will Be Boys

I think back to the four wrestlers and the stifling culture of masculinity in which they live. If schools were to radically alter this culture and substitute for it a new vision of masculinity, what would that look like? In this environment, boys would express a full range of behaviors and emotions without fear of being chastized. They would be permitted and encouraged to cry, to be afraid, to show joy, and to express love in a gentle fashion. Extreme concern for career goals would be replaced by a consideration of one's need for recreation, health, and meaningful work. Older boys would be encouraged to tutor and play with younger students. Moreover, boys would receive as much recognition for artistic talents as they do for athletics, and, in general, they would value leisure-time, recreational activities as highly as competitive sports.

In a system where maleness and femaleness were equally valued, boys might no longer feel that they have to "prove" themselves to other boys; they would simply accept the worth of each person and value those differences. Boys would realize that it is permissable to admit failure. In addition, they would seek out opportunities to learn from girls and women. Emotional support would be commonplace, and it would no longer be seen as just the role of the female to provide the support. Relationships between boys and girls would no longer be based on limited roles, but instead would become expressions of two individuals learning from and supporting one another. Relationships between boys would reflect their care for one another rather then their mutual fear and distrust.

Aggressive styles of resolving conflicts would be the exception rather than the norm. Girls would feel welcome in activities dominated by boys, knowing that they were safe from the threat of being sexually harassed. Boys would no longer boast of beating up another boy or of how much they "got off" of a girl the night before. In fact, the boys would be as outraged as the girls at rape or other violent crimes in the community. Finally, boys would become active in efforts to stop nuclear proliferation and all other forms of military violence, following the examples set by activist women.

The development of a new conception of masculinity based on this vision is an ambitious task, but one which is essential for the health and safety of both men and women. The survival of our society may rest on the degree to which we are able to teach men to cherish life.

Women

~

BY

ALICE

WALKER

They were women then
My mama's generation
Husky of voice—Stout of
Step
With fists as well as
Hands
How they battered down
Doors
And ironed
Starched white
Shirts
How they led
Armies
Headragged Generals
Across mined
Fields
Booby-trapped
Ditches
To discover books
Desks
A place for us
How they knew what we
Must know
Without knowing a page
Of it
Themselves

ACKNOWLEDGEMENTS

Care has been taken to trace ownership of copyright material contained in this text. The publishers will gladly accept any information that will enable them to rectify any reference or credit in subsequent editions.

TEXT

p. 1 "Notre Dame de Grâce" by Naomi Guttman. From *Reasons for Winter* by Naomi Guttman, Brick Books, 1991. Reprinted by permission of the publisher; **p. 3** "Shaping a Young Male Mind" by Bronwen Wallace. From *Arguments With the World: Essays by Bronwen Wallace* edited by Joanne Page. Reprinted by permission of Quarry Press Inc.; **p. 7** "Charles" by Shirley Jackson. From *The Lottery and Other Stories* by Shirley Jackson. Copyright © 1949 by Shirley Jackson. Copyright renewed © 1977 by Laurence Hyman, Barry Hyman, Mrs. Sarah Webster and Mrs. Joanne Schnurer. Reprinted by permission of Farrar, Straus & Giroux, Inc.; **p. 12** "Invisible Friends" from *Invisible Friends* by Alan Ayckbourn. Reprinted by permission of Faber and Faber Ltd.; **p. 15** "The Accident" by Joyce Marshall. From *Any Time At All* by Joyce Marshall. Used by permission of the Canadian Publishers, McClelland & Stewart, Toronto; **p. 24** "The Fisherman" by Richard Sommer. From *Sounding* by Richard Sommer, by permission of the authors; **p. 26** To Every Thing There Is a Season by Alistair MacLeod. From *As Birds Bring Forth The Sun* by Alistair MacLeod. Used by permission of the Canadian Publishers, McClelland & Stewart, Toronto; **p. 32** "Gaining Yardage" by Leo Dangel. From *Old Man Brunner Country* by Leo Dangel, published by Spoon River Poetry Press, 1987. Reprinted by permission of the author; **p. 34** "Quilters" by Barbara Damashek and Molly Newman © 1986, by Barbara Damashek & Molly Newman. Based on the book *The Quilters: Women and Domestic Art* © 1977, by Patricia Cooper Baker and Norma Buferd. Reprinted by permission of Helen Merrill, Ltd.; **p. 36** "You Just Don't Understand" by Deborah Tannen. From *You Just Don't Understand* by Deborah Tannen, Ph.D. Copyright © 1990 by Deborah Tannen, Ph.D. By Permission of William Morrow and Company, Inc.; **p. 43** "Chemical Reaction" by Bonnie Bishop. From *Elaborate Beasts* © 1988 Bonnie Bishop. Used by permission of Red Deer College Press.; **p. 44** "Young, Gay—and Alone" by Barry Came. *Maclean's Magazine*, Maclean Hunter Publishing Limited, February 22, 1993; **p. 48** "The Perilous Balancing Act of Growing Up Male" by Angela Phillips. Reprinted by permission of *The Guardian*; **p. 53** "The Fitness Industry's Empty Promise" by Jody Benjamin. *The Ottawa Citizen*, April 28, 1993; **p. 56** "Studies Find Body Builders Suffer 'Reverse Anorexia'" by Shelley Page. Reprinted by permission of *The Ottawa Citizen*; **p. 59** "Thin Equals Happy? Fat Chance" by Tess Fragoulis. Reprinted with permission of Tess Fragoulis; **p. 62** "The Selling of Addiction to Women" by Carol Moog. From *Media & Values*, Issue # 54-55, published by Center for Media Literacy. Reprinted with permission; **p. 70** "The Poet's Visit" by Nahid Rachlin. From *Veils* by Nahid Rachlin, City Lights Books, 1992. Reprinted by permission of the author; **p. 79** Excerpt from *The Lords of Discipline*. Copyright © 1980 by Pat Conroy. Reprinted by permission of Houghton Mifflin Company. All rights reserved; **p. 80** "The Bride" by Suniti Namjoshi. From *The Blue Donkey Fables* by Suniti Namjoshi, (London: The Women's Press, 1988). Reprinted by permission of the Author; **p. 81** "The Darling" by Anton Chekhov from *Anton Chekhov: Selected Stories by Anton Chekhov*, translated by Ann Dunnigan, Translation copyright © 1960 by Ann Dunnigan. Used by permission of Dutton Signet, a division of Penguin Books USA Inc.; **p.92** "Day of the Bride" by Joy Kogawa © Joy Kogawa; **p. 93** Excerpt from *Life After God* – Reprinted with the permission of Pocket Books, a Division of Simon & Schuster Inc. from *Life After God* by Douglas Coupland. Copyright © 1994 by Douglas Campbell Coupland; **p. 96** "My Father Writes to My Mother by Assia Djebar. Taken from *Fantasia*, published by Quartet Books Ltd. 1985; **p. 100** "Parlour Game" by Alden Nowlan. From *I'm a Stranger Here Myself* by Alden Nowlan, © 1974 Clarke, Irwin & Company Ltd. Reprinted by permission of Stoddart Publishing Co. Limited, 34 Lesmill Rd., Don Mills, Ont. M3B 2T6 Canada; **p. 102** "Seventeen Syllables" by Hisaye Yamamoto. From *Seventeen Syllables and Other Stories* by Hisaye Yamamoto, © 1988 by Hisaye Yamamoto DeSoto. Brooklyn, NY: Kitchen Table: Women of Color Press. Reprinted by permission of the author and of Kitchen Table: Women of Color Press, Box 40-4920, Brooklyn NY 11240. © Partisau Review, 1949; © renewed, Hisaye Yamamoto DeSoto, 1976; **p. 114** "Ten Years and More" by Miriam Waddington From *Collected Poems*, copyright © Miriam Waddington 1986. Reprinted by permission of Oxford University Press Canada; **p. 117** "Maidens" by Bonnie Bishop. From *Elaborate Beasts* © 1988 Bonnie Bishop. Used by permission of Red Deer College Press; **p. 118** "Here In My Arms" by Mary Melfi. From *A Queen is Holding a Mummified Cat* by Mary Melfi, Guernica Editions Inc., 1982. Reprinted by permission of the author & publisher; **p. 120** "Mother and I, Walking" by Lorna Crozier. From *Angels of Flesh, Angels of Silence* by Lorna Crozier. Used by permission of the Canadian Publishers, McClelland & Stewart, Toronto; **p. 121** "My Oedipus Complex" by Frank O'Connor. Reprinted by arrangement with Harriet O'Donovan Sheehy, c/o Joan Daves Agency as agent for the proprietor. Copyright 1981 by Frank O'Connor; **p. 136** "Johnnie's Poem" by Alden Nowlan. From *An Exchange of Gifts* by Alden Nowland , © Irwin Publishing Inc., 1985. Reprinted by permission of Stoddart Publishing Co. Limited, Don Mills, Ontario; **p. 138** "Potato Planters" by Lorna Crozier. From *Angels of Flesh, Angels of Silence* by Lorna Crozier. Used by permission of the Canadian Publishers, McClelland & Stewart, Toronto; **p. 140** "Excerpt from *Jin Guo: Voices of Chinese Canadian Women*, Copyright © 1992 Women's Book Committee, Chinese Canadian National Council. Reprinted by permission of the Women's Press; **p. 145** "Where Have All the Fathers Gone?" by Rebecca Baggett. Reprinted by permission of *Ms*. Magazine, Jan/Feb. 1993 issue; **p. 149** "Househusbands" by Randall Beach. This article originally appeared in the Hartford *Advocate*, an alternative weekly newspaper in Hartford, CT.; **p. 152** "Station" by Eamon Grennan. copyright 1992 by Eamon Grennan. Reprinted from *As If It Matters* with the permission of Graywolf Press, Saint Paul, Minnesota; **p. 154** "I Want to Go Home" by Clara Lovatt © 1992 Artemis Enterprises. Reprinted from *Mother of Thyme*, vol. II, No. 2, Winter 1992. RR #2, Box 54 Dundas, Ont. L9H 5E2. Used with permission; **p. 160** "Brothers" by Kate Braid. From *Covering Rough Ground* written by Kate Braid, published by Polestar Press Ltd., 1011 Commercial Dr., Vancouver, B.C. V5L 3X1, Canada; **p. 162** "First Day on a New Jobsite" by Susan Eisenberg © 1984 by Susan Eisenberg, reprinted by permission of the author. Originally appeared in *It's a Good Thing I'm Not Macho* (Whetstone Press, 1984) and reprinted in *Calling Home* edited by Janet Zandy (Rutgers, 1990); **p. 165** "Simmering" by Margaret Atwood © Margaret Atwood, 1983. Reprinted by permission of the Author. Originally published in *Murder in the Dark* (Coach House Press, 1983); **p. 168** "Who Teaches Primary?" by Cynthia Pratt Nicolson. Reprinted by permission of Cynthia Prath Nicolson; **p. 172** "Invisible Woman, Crossing Borders" by Jean Molesky-Poz. Originally appeared in Chicago Review, Vol 39, Nos. 3 & 4, 1993. Reprinted by permission of the author; **p. 179** "'Liberating' Science" by Andrea Schluter © 1994 by Andrea Schluter. By permission of the author; **p. 183** "Why Men Are Hogging the Digital Highway" by David Plotnikoff. Reprinted by permission: Tribune Media Services; **p. 188** "This Is Not Final" by Fran Davis. Reprinted by permission of Frances Davis; **p. 191** "Out of the Woods" by Jodi L. Jacobson. From *World Watch*, Nov./Dec. 1992 issue. Reprinted by permission; **p. 200** "The Poets in the Kitchen" by Paule Marshall. Reprinted with the permission of the author; **p. 209** "Rella Braithwaite 1923" as told to Dionne Brand. From *No Burden to Carry* by Dionne Brand, 1991. Reprinted by permission of the Women's Press; **p. 219** "Listening...an Interview with Bertha Petiquan" by Mark Dowie © Mark Dowie 1994; **p. 225** "The Rites of Sisterhood" by Naomi Wolf. Reprinted from *NEXT: Young American Writers on the New Generation*, edited by Eric Liu, with the permission of Naomi Wolf and W.W. Norton & Company, Inc. Copyright © 1994 by Naomi Wolf; **p. 233** "A New Vision of Masculinity" by Cooper Thompson. By permission of the author. Cooper Thompson is a trainer/consultant in the areas of homophobia, racism, and sexism from the perspective of being heterosexual, White and male. He lives in Cambridge, Massachusetts; **p. 242** "Women by Alice Walker from *Revolutionary Petunias & Other Poems*, copyright © 1970 by Alice Walker. Reprinted by permission of Harcourt Brace & Company.

PHOTOGRAPHS
p. 4, 42, 47, 50, 79, 95, 116, 119, 137, 148, 159, 161, 171, 190, 224, 241, 243 all by Dick Hemingway; p. 199 Robert Garrard.